The Pub League Quiz Book Number 4

Quiz Masters of Great Britain

foulsham

LONDON • NEW YORK • TORONTO • SYDNEY

foulsham

Yeovil Road, Slough, Berkshire SL1 4JH

ISBN 0-572-01760-X

Copyright © 1992 Quiz Masters of Great Britain

Printed in Great Britain at St Edmundsbury Press,
Bury St Edmunds

Contents

The Pub League Quizzes

The Answers

The Pub League Quizzes

Rules of the Game

These exciting quizzes are taken from the QuizMasters Pub League quizzes. They are great fun to play at home with any number of team members, or you can use the correct pub league rules and try out the quizzes at your local.

If you play in a league, all the games are played on the same day at the same time. Questions are supplied in a sealed envelope to be opened by the question master in the presence of both teams at the beginning of the match. The questions and answers are normally listed together on a single sheet which is only seen by the question master. We have separated them in the book so that a team member can read out the questions, if necessary, when you are playing at home.

TEAMS
Each team consists of four playing members. In addition, a question master/timekeeper is provided by the home team, and both teams supply a scorer (or the team captains can keep score).

RULES
The match is played in two halves. The questions master tosses a coin to see who plays first.

The first four rounds in each half are team rounds. There are five questions for each team, which are asked to each team alternately. Conferring is allowed. If the team cannot answer, or answers incorrectly, the question is passed over to the other team for a bonus.

The final round in each half is a round of individual questions. The team which answers first, answers the individual questions in the first half, and the opposing team answers the individual questions in the second half. At the beginning of the match, each team member chooses his or her subject for the individual round from the five categories provided. Conferring is not allowed on these questions. If they cannot answer the questions, or answer incorrectly, the questions can be passed over to the other team for a bonus, and all the opposing team can confer.

All answers to the team questions and to bonus questions must be given by the team captains.

TIMING

30 seconds is allowed for each answer, which starts after the question has been read out. An additional 15 seconds is allowed if the question is passed over for a bonus.

SCORING

All correct team questions:	2 points
All correct individual questions:	3 points
All correct bonus questions:	1 point.

The question master acts as the adjudicator and his decision is final. If he makes a mistake which would result in a question being unfair, he can replace it with one of the reserve questions provided.

Teams use the score sheets provided to keep scores. The scorers check and agree the points after each round. You can copy the score sheet provided for home use.

THE DRINKS ROUND

Questions are also provided for a drinks round. These are not counted as part of the match, but can be used as reserve questions if necessary. There are ten questions for each team, which are asked alternately.

Pub League Quiz Score Sheet

1st HALF	HOME		AWAY	
ROUND 1	SCORE	BONUS	SCORE	BONUS
Q1				
Q2				
Q3				
Q4				
Q5				
TOTAL				
ROUND 2				
Q1				
Q2				
Q3				
Q4				
Q5				
TOTAL				
ROUND 3				
Q1				
Q2				
Q3				
Q4				
Q5				
TOTAL				
ROUND 4				
Q1				
Q2				
Q3				
Q4				
Q5				
TOTAL				
ROUND 5				
Q1				
Q2				
Q3				
Q4				
Q5				
TOTAL				
1st HALF	HOME		AWAY	
TOTAL				

FINAL SCORE: _____ Home Team _____ Away Team _____

2nd HALF	HOME		AWAY	
ROUND 6	SCORE	BONUS	SCORE	BONUS
Q1				
Q2				
Q3				
Q4				
Q5				
TOTAL				
ROUND 7				
Q1				
Q2				
Q3				
Q4				
Q5				
TOTAL				
ROUND 8				
Q1				
Q2				
Q3				
Q4				
Q5				
TOTAL				
ROUND 9				
Q1				
Q2				
Q3				
Q4				
Q5				
TOTAL				
ROUND 10				
Q1				
Q2				
Q3				
Q4				
Q5				
TOTAL				
2nd HALF	HOME		AWAY	
TOTAL				

Pub League Quiz 1

The individual questions are in Rounds 5 and 10 and are on the following subjects: Abbreviations, Mythology, Sport, News of the 80s and United Kingdom.

Team 1 | *Team 2*

ROUND 1

1 Which food product did Gail Borden give to the world in 1858?

2 Who achieved fame in 1920 by the publication of a collection of stories called *Bliss*?

3 Who plays Lt. Skinner in TV's *In the Heat of the Night*?

4 Which countries heroes are celebrated in Luis de Camoens' poem 'The Lusiads'?

5 In a standard pack of cards, if 17 red cards have been played, how many red cards are left?

1 What was Johann Gutenberg the first European to invent?

2 Who wrote the poem 'Not Waving but Drowning'?

3 In which TV serial did Ian Hendry and Wanda Ventham co-star?

4 Who helped her father rescue shipwreck survivors off the Farne Island in September 1838?

5 Add together the number of players in a rugby union side and the number in a rugby league side. What is the total?

ROUND 2

1 Which two pop stars recorded 'Don't Go Breaking My Heart' in 1976.

2 What nationality was the first explorer to

1 Which pop singer recorded the album, 'Silverbird' in 1973?

2 With the deserts of which continent are the

sight the Grand Canyon?

3 Who was George IV's last Prime Minister?

4 Which comic actor starred as Headmaster in the 1985 film *Clockwise*?

5 Which is the most commonly used punctuation mark in the English language?

ROUND 3

1 What is Mons Meg?

2 Which mountain can you see from a train called 'The Bullet'?

3 Who wrote the novel *Phantom of the Opera* in 1911?

4 Which military conflict forms the background for Shakespeare's *Troilus and Cressida*?

5 Which World War II leader was killed with his mistress Clara Petacci?

ROUND 4

1 Which country left the Commonwealth in 1961?

2 What is a homonym?

names Charles Sturt and Robert O'Hara Burke associated?

3 Who was Queen Victoria's first Prime Minister?

4 Which 1986 film told the story of rock 'n' roll singer Richie Valens?

5 Which letter it the English alphabet went by the name izzard?

1 Where can Mons Meg be seen today?

2 What did the B & O Railroad's initials stand for?

3 What are the surnames of 'The Two Ronnies'?

4 What is the 'sack' of which Sir John Falstaff is so fond in Shakespeare's *Henry IV*?

5 How do we usually contract 'Gehime Staatspolizei?

1 Which country left the Commonwealth in 1972?

2 What is hyperbole?

3 Which novel by Stephen Crane won him immediate recognition when it was published?

3 Which 18th century novelist wrote *Roderick Random*, *Peregrine Pickle* and *Humphry Clinker*?

4 What nationality was the artist Paul Klee?

4 What nationality was the artist Wassily Kandinsky?

5 What is the home of a fox called?

5 What is the home of a beaver called?

ROUND 5 *Individual questions for team 1*

Abbreviations
What does the abbreviation SPCK stand for?

Mythology
The God Anubis was represented by the Egyptians as having a man's body and the head of what?

Sport
How many hoops are used in a game of croquet?

News of the 80s
In July 1984, lightning was blamed for a fire which badly damaged which famous British cathedral?

United Kingdom
Where is the head office of the Premium Savings Bonds?

Team 2	Team 1

ROUND 6

1 Which American playwright achieved a start on Broadway with *Come Blow Your Horn*?

1 Which playwright wrote the 1958 play *The Hostage*?

2 What does Toc H stand for?

2 Who founded Toc H?

3 In which year did the half crown cease to be legal tender?

3 In which year did Great Britain get commercial TV?

4 Which animal is often known as 'Brock'?

5 Name the character played by Jamie Farr in TV's *M.A.S.H.*

4 What kind of creature is a red-bellied tamarin?

5 Name the shop assistant portrayed by Wendy Richard in *Are You Being Served?*

ROUND 7

1 What night precedes May Day?

2 How many grains go into a scruple?

3 Who was originally known as Giovanni Bernardone?

4 Who was sentenced to a three-day prison term in 1989, for slapping a policeman?

5 What is the correct heraldic name for the colour blue?

1 When is Labour Day?

2 How many yards in a chain?

3 Which Basque Jesuit missionary was known as 'The Apostle of the Indies'?

4 Which Sunday newspaper made its first appearance in September 1989?

5 What is the correct heraldic name for the colour black?

ROUND 8

1 Which bank shares went on sale to the public for the first time in October 1986?

2 Who played the original Liver Birds?

3 What is the meaning of the phrase 'Caviare to the General'?

4 Which English composer, in 1923, wrote a piece for speaker and chamber orchestra called *Facade*?

1 During the 1980s, which British industry claimed 'We're getting there' in an advertising slogan?

2 Which comedian was known for his 'odd odes'?

3 What was meant by the saying, 'He was with the colours'?

4 Which Norwegian composer wrote the incidental music for Ibsen's drama, *Peer Gynt*?

11

5 What replaced the Royal Army Service Corps in 1965?

5 Which branch of the British Army is known as The Gunners?

ROUND 9

1 What is the maximum number of overs each side is allowed to bowl in a Benson & Hedges Cup match?

1 How many counties contest the County Championship in cricket, from 1992?

2 What type of aircraft did Spain's Juan de la Cierva invent?

2 What nickname was given to the first Soviet supersonic airliner?

3 The Lek is the currency of which country?

3 The Baht is the currency of which country?

4 Which sport is known in France as 'Le jeu de paume'?

4 Which sport does the PRCA represent?

5 Who stopped Bjorn Borg's string of Wimbledon singles wins?

5 Who was the jockey featured in the film *Champions*?

ROUND 10   *Individual questions for team 2*

Abbreviations
What does FRSL stand for?

Mythology
In Greek mythology, King Minos of Crete demanded a payment every 9 years. What form did this take?

Sport
Which two players are allowed to score in a game of netball?

News of the 80s
Who won the Greenwich by-election for the SDP in February 1987?

United Kingdom
Which city lies at the mouth of the River Lagan?

Team 1

DRINKS ROUND

1 Into which sea does the Danube flow?
2 Which member of 'Cream' was a 'Yardbird'?
3 Who was responsible for nationalising The Suez Canal?
4 Whose three sons were Shem, Ham and Japheth?
5 Which orange liqueur is based on fine cognac?
6 Which bird is the national symbol of France?
7 Which 'National Park' did Yogi Bear call home?
8 Which volcano buried the city of Pompeii in AD 79?
9 Who painted *The Garden of Earthly Delights*?
10 In which sport are the terms 'raiders', 'antis' and 'cant' used?

Team 2

1 Of which ocean is the Sargasso Sea part?
2 Who was the lead singer with 'The Who'?
3 Of which country was the House of Hapsburg the ruling dynasty?
4 To which town does *A Town Like Alice* refer?
5 What flavour is the liqueur Framboise?
6 The Hibiscus is the State flower of which American State?
7 Which Disney cartoon saw two animals eating spaghetti at Tony's Restaurant?
8 Who was Roman Procurator of Judea from AD 26 to AD 36?
9 What does the painting *The Battle of Gettysburg* claim to be?
10 What mechanical system did George Ligowsky invent, in 1880, for marksmen?

RESERVE QUESTIONS

1 Which was the world's largest airline in the 1980s?
2 Who had a hit with 'I'm the Urban Spaceman'?
3 Who wrote the Overture *Roman Carnival*?

Pub League Quiz 2

The individual questions are in Rounds 5 and 10 and are on the following subjects: Television, Sport, Plants, Religion and Words.

Team 1

Team 2

ROUND 1

1 What was the name of the first ship to be propelled by steam turbines?
2 Which author created the detective Sergeant Cluff?
3 In which fictional town is *Crown Court* set?
4 In which country is the volcano Cotopaxi?
5 Who has won both the Nobel Peace Prize and the Nobel Prize for Chemistry?

1 What was the name of the first vessel designed by Nansen to winter in the polar ice?
2 Which author created the detective Van der Valk?
3 In which town is 'The Little House on the Prairie'?
4 In which country is the mountain Nanda Devi?
5 A new Nobel Prize was introduced in 1969; what discipline does it cover?

ROUND 2

1 Who first sang about a 'Lady in Red'?
2 Which writer created Mary Poppins?
3 What is the monetary unit of Sierra Leone?
4 Which Tennis champion of the 1920s and 30s was nicknamed 'Big Bill'?

1 Who sang the theme song to the movie *Fame*?
2 Who created Mowgli?
3 What s the monetary unit of Kuwait?
4 Which Boxer was nicknamed 'The Sepia Slayer?'

5 Which UK entrant sang 'Jack-In-A-Box' in the Eurovision Song Contest?

5 Who had his first hit album with 'The 12-Year-Old Genius'?

ROUND 3

1 Which Florentine statesman wrote *The Prince*?

1 Which British statesman wrote *Coningsby*?

2 Chaim Weizmann was the President of which country?

2 Marshal Pilsudski was Head of State of which country?

3 Who played Robin Hood in the first British TV series?

3 In which film did Humphrey Bogart play a vampire?

4 Who was the first Democrat President of the USA?

4 Which American President was assassinated in 1901?

5 In which sport would you find coppers, corners and landlords?

5 In which sport is the Iroquois Cup awarded?

ROUND 4

1 Which city is graced by Michelangelo's 'David'?

1 Name the Florentine sculptor and goldsmith whose autobiography was not published until more than 150 years after his death.

2 Which fictional mad medical man grafted animals and people together to make man-beasts?

2 Which fictional medical man took his family to Siberia during the Russian revolution?

3 What is the correct chemical name for Saltpetre?

3 What is the correct chemical name for Epsom salts?

4 Which member of the Royal Family took part in the radio programme *The Archers*?

5 Which actor had a British hit in 1971 with 'The Way You Look Tonight'?

4 Which member of the Royal Family opened the new Falkland Island's airport in 1985?

5 Which actor had a hit in 1968 with 'MacArthur Park'?

ROUND 5   *Individual questions for team 1*

Television
Which TV series contained the line, 'I am not a number, I am a free man'?

Sport
What sporting body was founded at the Star & Garter Coffee House in Pall Mall in 1750?

Plants
What is the common name for the Digitalis plant?

Religion
In which religion do 'Vishnu' and 'Siva' play a major role?

Words
What is 'dendrochronology'?

Team 2	Team 1

ROUND 6

1 What was the 1984 sequel to *2001. A Space Odyssey*?

2 Which town in South Australia became the home of the Long Range Weapons Establishment in 1946?

3 Who wrote plays called

1 Which film released in 1986 was the sequel to *Romancing the Stone*?

2 What large flat area of Australia has a name which comes from the Latin for 'no tree'?

3 Who wrote the play in

The Circle and *The Constant Wife*?

4 Who wrote *The Old Wives' Tale*?

5 Which actor starred in both the stage and film productions of *Cabaret*?

blank verse, *Tamburlaine the Great*?

4 Who wrote *Children of The New Forest*?

5 Which actress starred with Woody Allen in both the stage and film versions of *Play It Again, Sam*?

ROUND 7

1 Which Italian landmark has nearly 300 steps?

2 From which ballet does *The Dying Swan* come?

3 What year did Concorde make its first scheduled supersonic flight?

4 Which artist painted *Mrs Pelham feeding Chickens*?

5 What does 'aardvark' mean in English?

1 Where is the famous Hall of Mirrors?

2 What was unusual about Stravinsky's *Circus Polka* ballet?

3 What year did man first walk on the moon?

4 Which Venetian artist is noted for his paintings of London?

5 What does 'pterodactyl' mean in English?

ROUND 8

1 How many dice are used in poker dice?

2 Which African country takes its name from the Lion?

3 Which 1963 film told the story of the defence of Rorke's Drift?

4 From which plant family does natural vanilla flavouring come?

1 To what number do the opposite sides of a die always add up?

2 Which is the largest town in Alaska?

3 Who starred opposite Jane Fonda in the film *Klute*?

4 What kind of fruit is a kumquat?

5 After which US President is New Hampshire's highest mountain named?

5 On which peak did Noah's Ark come to rest?

ROUND 9

1 Which TV series featured novice trail boss Rowdy Yates?

1 Who played the title role in TV's *Bronco*?

2 Where, in Britain, are the Elgin Marbles?

2 Who was the 'Flanders Mare'?

3 Who wrote *No Highway*?

3 Who wrote *Waverley*?

4 What does T.T.D. mean on a doctor's prescription?

4 What does ECG stand for?

5 What is the positive square root of 676?

5 What is the positive square root of 529?

ROUND 10 *Individual questions for team 2*

Television
What were the forenames of 'The Likely Lads'?

Sport
In which year did 'Aldaniti' win the Grand National?

Plants
Which plant was featured on the reverse side of the three-penny piece minted between 1937 and 1967?

Religion
What is St Patrick said to have used to explain the 'Trinity'?

Words
What would a Scotsman do with a 'spurtle'?

Team 1   *Team 2*

DRINKS ROUND

1 Where in Britain was King Alfred buried?

1 Where in Britain would you find Bolton Abbey?

2 Who murdered Thomas à Becket?

2 Who murdered William the Silent, Prince of Orange?

3 Bob Hoskins won Best Actor award at the 1986 Cannes Film Festival for his part in which film?

3 Which 1985 film was all about the kidnapping of a pig?

4 In 1866, a decoration was instituted for gallantry in saving life at sea or on land. What is it called?

4 Which decoration, intended for civilians and instituted in 1940, is worn before all others except the VC?

5 Where in the human body would you find the metatarsals?

5 Where in the body would you find the carpals?

6 How much of the Earth's surface is covered with water?

6 Which is the smallest of the Earth's oceans?

7 What is the name of the PM in 'Yes Prime Minister'?

7 Whom did Michael Parkinson replace as host of *Give Us A Clue*?

8 Where is the annual dog sled champion-ship race held?

8 What did Dr Vivian Fuchs achieve in 99 days in 1957/58?

9 By what name is Bernadette Soubirous now known?

9 What name did the ballerina Lilian Alicia Marks adopt?

10 In which country would you find the Gersoppa Falls?

10 In which country would you find the Staubbach Falls?

RESERVE QUESTIONS

1 Who is the patron saint of Russia?
2 Who designed the tapestry for the rebuilt Coventry Cathedral?
3 Which Shipping Forecast lies immediately to the south of 'Fisher'?

Pub League Quiz 3

The individual questions are in Rounds 5 and 10 and are on the following subjects: Films, Which year?, Scandal, Capitals and Science.

Team 1

Team 2

ROUND 1

1 In which Alpine resort did France's Jean-Claude Killy win three Olympic golds in 1968?

1 In which French resort were the first World Nordic Ski Championships held, in 1924?

2 Which scientific instrument did Hans and Zacharias Janssen invent in 1590?

2 Which plastic material did John Wesley Hyatt develop in 1870?

3 Which Gilbert and Sullivan operetta has the subtitle *The Peer and the Peri*?

3 Which Gilbert and Sullivan operetta has the subtitle *The King of Barataria*?

4 Which European border reopened in February 1985 after 16 years?

4 In January 1986, George Younger succeeded Michael Heseltine in which Cabinet post?

5 Which hero said, 'England expects every man will do his duty'?

5 Who galloped towards Lexington in April 1755 to warn that the British were coming?

ROUND 2

1 In the TV series, where did Dr Finlay live?

1 In which city does Mike Hammer work?

2 The Kalahari Desert lies mainly in which African country?

2 On which side of the Andes does the Atacama Desert lie?

3 Which sport would you

3 From which sport does

expect to see in a velodrome?

4 What is 88 in Roman numerals?

5 What did Mencken describe as, 'The theory that common people know what they want, and deserve to get it good and hard'?

the phrase 'to win hands down' come?

4 In Roman numerals, what is MMM minus MD?

5 What did Mencken describe as, 'The ransom that the happy pay to the devil'?

ROUND 3

1 Which Italian cruise ship was hijacked by a PLO group in 1985?
2 Which popular musician played 'Alias' in the film, *Pat Garrett and Billy the Kid*?
3 Who created the cartoon character 'Blondie'?
4 Which country's national sport is hurling?
5 Who was Donalbain's father in *Macbeth*?

1 Which Greenpeace campaign ship was sunk in Auckland in 1985?
2 Whose first hit single was 'Mandy' in 1974?

3 Which comic strip super hero did C.C. Beck create?
4 Which country dominated Olympic hockey from 1928 until 1960?
5 Who agreed to marry Benedick at the end of *Much Ado About Nothing*?

ROUND 4

1 Which TV comedy series takes place in a London barber's shop?
2 Which palace was founded on the site of James I's mulberry orchard?

1 Who played Col. Hall in TV's *Bilko*?

2 Where was the original site of Marble Arch?

3 In which European country is the famous Jungfraujoch Railway Station?

4 Which British woman tennis star was five times runner-up in the World Table Tennis Championships?

5 In which year did the old sixpenny coin cease to be legal tender in Britain?

3 Which European country has a fast train known by the initials TGV?

4 Who won the 1991 New York Women's Marathon?

5 The 900th Anniversary of which book was celebrated in 1986?

ROUND 5 *Individual questions for team 1*

Films
In which musical film will you hear the song 'Always true to you in my fashion'?

Which year?
In which year did Fidel Castro come to power in Cuba?

Scandal
Which English king illegally married Mrs Fitzherbert?

Capitals
What is the Capital of Malta?

Science
What do you call the positive-charged particle which is a constituent of the nucleus of an atom?

Team 2	*Team 1*

ROUND 6

1 Which character does Mrs Danny DeVito play in TV's *Cheers*?

2 Which Stone provided the key to translating

1 What is Mrs DeVito's stage name?

2 Which fossil remains, found in 1908, were

Egyptian hieroglyphics?

3 Which country declared war on the Allies in June 1940 and Germany in October 1943?

4 Which nation won football's World Cup in 1982?

5 In 1984 which Indian city was the scene of the chemical works tragedy in which thousands died?

ROUND 7

1 What is the meaning of the cooking term 'farci'?

2 What is the name of George Knightley's home in Jane Austin's novel *Emma*?

3 Which actress played Sid James' wife in TV's *Bless This House*?

4 Of which country was Olof Palme Prime Minister?

5 Which Beaufort number relates to 'Moderate breeze'?

ROUND 8

1 Izaak Walton, who died in 1683, has been called the father of which sport?

shown to be a forgery in 1955?

3 Who betrayed Norway to the Nazis in World War II?

4 Who were the English league football Champions 1984/5 and 1986/7?

5 In which year was the first 'Hands across Britain' demonstration against unemployment?

1 From which animal does 'prosciutto' come?

2 In which novel did Emile Zola depict life in a French mining community?

3 Who hosted *The $64,000 Question* on British TV?

4 Of which country was Adolphe Thiers the President?

5 Which Beaufort number relates to 'Calm'?

1 For which sport is the Wisden Annual published?

23

2 What colour is the gem stone Amethyst?

3 Who was Mozart's great rival in *Amadeus*?

4 What is 19 squared?

5 Name Frankie Goes To Hollywood's 1984 album.

2 What colour is the gemstone Lapis lazuli?

3 Who wrote *Schindler's Ark*?

4 What is the positive square root of 484?

5 Name Helen Reddy's 1972 hit album.

ROUND 9

1 Greece joined the EEC; France abolished capital punishment; and the Newcastle metro opened; which year?

2 Which American artist painted *The Biglen Brothers Racing*?

3 Who became British Shadow Foreign Secretary in July 1987?

4 Which composer described his *The Dream of Gerontius* as 'The best of me'?

5 Who was Starsky and Hutch's nark?

1 Death of Donald Campbell; the *Torrey Canyon* disaster; and China exploded her first H-bomb; which year?

2 Which female American Impressionist artist was famous for her mother and child paintings?

3 Who became Britain's Secretary of State for Energy in June 1987?

4 Which composer's first opera, *Orfeo*, was produced in 1607?

5 Terry Gilliam provided the animation for which TV comedy team?

ROUND 10 *Individual questions for team 2*

Films

What's the name of the 1986 British musical based on teenagers' lives in the 1950s?

Which year?
In which year did Great Britain get its first Labour Government?

Scandal
In the 1988 film, *Scandal*, which real-life person was played by Bridget Fonda?

Capitals
What is the capital of Sri Lanka?

Science
What is the coil of an electric motor or dynamo called?

Team 1   **Team 2**

DRINKS ROUND

1 What sport contests the Leonard Trophy?

2 Where did the League of Nations establish its Permanent Court of International Justice?

3 Who was the Nymph who changed into a laurel bush?

4 In musical terms what does '*lento*' mean?

5 On which river does the town of Plock stand?

6 In nautical terms, what is a 'grapnel'?

7 For whose household did Mr Hudson and Mrs Bridges work?

1 What unusual thing happened in the 1877 Boat Race?

2 Which international organisation was established in Addis Ababa in 1963?

3 Who was King of Sparta and husband of Helen of Troy?

4 In musical terms what does '*presto*' mean?

5 On which river is Yonkers?

6 In nautical terms what is a 'hawser'?

7 For which school was Mr Potter the caretaker?

8 Which King of England was called 'the Hammer of the Scots'?

9 Where was the Derby run during World War II?

10 In which year did it become compulsory, in Britain, to wear front seat belts in cars?

8 Which King of England had the nickname 'Longshanks'?

9 The Eclipse Stakes is normally run where?

10 In which year was Prince Henry of Wales born?

RESERVE QUESTIONS

1 Who invented the radio valve in 1904?
2 Which Second World War bomber was nicknamed the 'Wimpey'?
3 To which group of plants does the Christmas Rose belong?

Pub League Quiz 4

The individual questions are in Rounds 5 and 10 and are on the following subjects: General knowledge, Counties, Space travel, British Prime Ministers and Abbreviations.

Team 1

Team 2

ROUND 1

1   Who wrote the music for the ballet *Coppélia*?

1   Who composed the orchestral suite *Karelia*?

2   Who became Archbishop of York in 1956, and in 1961 Archbishop of Canterbury?

2   What was the name of the black militant nationalist who was shot dead in New York City in 1965?

3   What are dulse and carrageen?

3   What is pumpernickel?

4   Who wrote *Auf Wiedersehen Pet*?

4   What was unusual about Barry's best man in *Auf Wiedersehen Pet*?

5   Who was wooed by Freddy Eynsford Hill in *Pygmalion*?

5   How was N.S. Norway better known?

ROUND 2

1   In sporting terms, what is a 'flying mare'?

1   What name is given to the playing objects in curling?

2   Where are the Drakensberg Mountains?

2   Where are the Eastern and Western Ghats?

3   Which actress starred opposite Humphrey Bogart in *The Maltese Falcon*?

3   Which actress starred opposite Charlie Chaplin in *Limelight*?

4 Who was the first Labour Premier to form a government?

5 Which British bird builds the smallest nests?

4 Who was the Aztec Emperor when the Spanish invaded Mexico?

5 Which is the largest British amphibian?

ROUND 3

1 What was the first of Paul Simons' ways to leave your lover?

2 Which successful London Lord Mayor, entrepreneur and philanthropist married Alice Fitzwarren?

3 In J M Barrie's play, who was the resourceful butler to Lord Loam?

4 What is the name of René's wife in 'Allo, 'Allo?

5 With which type of whiskey is a mint julep made?

1 Who was born John Henry Deutschendorf, Jr., and married Annie Martell?

2 Whose trial, on a charge of libelling Oscar Wilde, was to lead to Wilde going to prison himself?

3 Who married Edgar Linton in *Wuthering Heights*?

4 What is the famous painting in 'Allo, 'Allo, known as?

5 What are the two alcoholic ingredients of a Sidecar cocktail?

ROUND 4

1 Of which secret society did Nathan B. Forrest become the first leader in 1866?

2 For which country did Maharajah Ranjitsinhji play Test Cricket?

3 In which Hitchcock film did James Stewart play

1 What was the nickname given to the special force of police deployed in Ireland in 1920?

2 Name the Canadian variation of Lacrosse, which has six players in a team.

3 In *What Ever Happened to Baby Jane*, who was

a detective with a fear of heights?

4 What would you get if you mixed saltpetre, charcoal and sulphur?

5 What colour is a wild canary?

served a rat for lunch by Bette Davis?

4 Which metal is obtained from the ore cinnabar?

5 What does a bird use to grind its food?

ROUND 5   *Individual questions for team 1*

General knowledge
At sea, if you took the First Dog Watch, what time would you start?

Counties
Bristol is the administrative headquarters of which English county?

Space travel
What was the name of the space station launched by the Americans on 25th May 1973?

British Prime Ministers
To which political party did Prime Minister Herbert Asquith belong?

Abbreviations
In shipping, what does P & O stand for?

Team 2	Team 1

ROUND 6

1 What is dredging in culinary terms?

1 Within 4 degrees Celsius, at what temperature does the pasteurization of milk take place?

2 Who had a Christmas hit in 1969 with 'Two little Boys'?

2 Who had a Christmas hit in 1976 with 'When a Child is Born'?

3 Which historic locomotive was featured in a 1927 Buster Keaton film?

4 Which Verdi opera contains 'The Chorus of The Hebrew Slaves' ('Va Pensiero')?

5 Name the longest-running musical programme on British TV.

3 Which operate singer had a private waiting room at Craig-y-Nos railway station?

4 Which Saint Saens opera is set in Palestine?

5 Name the character who is leader of TV's *Fairly Secret Army*.

ROUND 7

1 In Bowls, what does the term 'Jack-high' mean?

1 In which sport do you find a tin, a service box and a telltale?

2 If an American recipe tells you to 'broil' a dish how should you cook it?

2 In corned beef, what does 'corned' mean?

3 Who was the Flag Captain of *HMS Victory* at Trafalgar?

3 Who was Sir John Gielgud's famous actress great-aunt?

4 Who was killed in a plane crash in 1967 along with most of his backing group, the Bar-Kays?

4 Which member of the Byrds was killed by a truck in 1973?

5 In which year did Amy Johnson make her solo flight from London to Australia?

5 In which year did Sheila Scott become the First British woman to fly solo around the world?

ROUND 8

1 Which bumbling TV detective does Peter Falk play?

1 Which TV Western centred on The Cartwright family?

2 Where in South

2 In which city would you

America is Welsh spoken?

3 What was Paul Muni a Fugitive from, in the 1932 film?

4 Which creature has the largest eyes?

5 What or who shrieked and squeaked in 50 different sharps and flats?

ROUND 9

1 Who succeeded Georges Pompidou as French President?

2 How many dancers perform 'The dance of the Cygnets' in the ballet, *Swan Lake*?

3 Which British building celebrated its 900th anniversary in 1965?

4 In which TV soap opera did Ryan O'Neal and Mia Farrow star?

5 Which Stravinsky ballet caused a riot at its first performance in 1913?

find a store called GUM?

3 What was the name of Goldfinger's bodyguard in the film?

4 Which small bird can fly backwards?

5 Who lived in a forest and tried to trap a Heffalump?

1 Who was the 4th man in the Burgess, Maclean, Philby scandal?

2 Which Hungarian-born composer and pianist took holy orders in 1865?

3 What was introduced in Britain on 1st April 1973?

4 Which TV series was a saga about the Seaton family in the north-east during the depression?

5 As what did Gustav Holst describe Saturn?

ROUND 10   *Individual questions for team 2*

General knowledge
Who told Ptolemy I that there was no royal road to geometry?

Counties
In area, which is the smallest English county?

Space travel
Yuri Gagarin was the first man in space. What was his spacecraft called?

British Prime Ministers
Which British Prime Minister was assassinated in 1812?

Abbreviations
What does FRAM stand for?

Team 1	Team 2

DRINKS ROUND

1 Which is the only South American country with both Pacific and Caribbean coastlines?

2 In which country did Brazil last win the World Cup?

3 Whose quater-centenary was celebrated in Britain on April 23nd 1964?

4 'The Fly' was a 1991 hit for which group?

5 In which film did Jack Nicholson play the caretaker of The Overlook Hotel?

6 What was the name of 'She Who Must Be Obeyed' in Rider Haggard's book *She*?

1 What is the name of the region of the southern oceans where strong prevailing westerlies blow?

2 Which British ice dancers won the World, Olympic and European titles in 1984?

3 Which British city was affected by a typhoid outbreak in May 1964?

4 'Everything I do' was top of the charts in 1991 for whom?

5 In which Dirty Harry film did Tyne Daly co-star with Clint Eastwood?

6 Which legal character refers to his wife as 'She Who Must Be Obeyed'?

7 What is the traditional Thanksgiving dessert in the USA?

8 What is the official language of Andorra?

9 The Royal Engineers are known as Sappers. What did 'to sap' originally mean?

10 What was the name of the motel in *Psycho*?

7 Which cake is named after a legendary girl from Bath?

8 What is the actual translation of terracotta?

9 Roman gladiators took their name from the gladius. What type of weapon was a gladius?

10 What was Elvis Presley's first film called?

RESERVE QUESTIONS

1 Which tree was sacred to the Druids?

2 What does 'Koh-i-noor', the name given to the famous diamond, mean?

3 In which children's TV series was there a snail named Brian and a cow named Ermintrude?

Pub League Quiz 5

The individual questions are in Rounds 5 and 10 and are on the following subjects. The Bible, Words, Literature, History and Sport.

Team 1	Team 2

ROUND 1

1 Who had a hit in 1967 with 'This is my Song'?

2 In which poem by Robert Browning would you find the lines 'God's in his heaven – All's right with the world'?

3 In which country would you find the River Vistula?

4 George Peppard played which insurance investigator on TV?

5 The oldest known living tree was named after which Biblical character?

1 Who had a hit in 1969 with 'In the Year 2525'?

2 In which poem by W.H. Davies would you find the lines 'What is this life if full of care'?

3 In which country would you find the Clutha River?

4 Which actor played private eye Frank Cannon on TV?

5 Which Cherokee Indian leader gave his name to a tree?

ROUND 2

1 Which ancient city had the famous Lion Gate?

2 Who was 'Old Bald Peg'?

3 Which country's air force was destroyed on the ground in June 1967?

1 Which was the oldest of the Greek orders of architecture?

2 What was Sandra Primo's sport?

3 Who challenged President Truman's conduct of the Korean War and was fired for it?

4 Which song from the film *Lovers and Other Strangers*, was awarded an Oscar in 1970?

5 On which island country would you find Adam's Peak?

ROUND 3

1 How wide is the goal in Polo?

2 In a church or cathedral, where would you find a 'reredos'?

3 What was the remarkable venue for the meeting of Napoleon and the Czar of Russia in Tilsit, July 1807?

4 In which city is the Jacques Cartier Bridge, opened in 1930?

5 *The Raft of Medusa* and *The Epsom Derby* are among the works of which artist?

ROUND 4

1 Which American State's song is 'Yankee Doodle Dandy'?

2 Which opera by Benjamin Britten includes characters known as Swallow, Hobson and Auntie?

4 Which song, from the film *Thank God it's Friday*, was awarded an Oscar in 1978?

5 Mount Hekla is an active volcano in which country?

1 What, in Baseball, is a 'Switch hitter'?

2 In which country of the world did the Coptic Church originate?

3 On which two islands was Napoleon imprisoned in 1814 and 1815 respectively?

4 Where are the Aleutian Islands?

5 *The Murdered Marat in his Bath* and *The Coronation of Napoleon* are among the works of which artist?

1 Which American State's song is 'Home on the Range'?

2 Name the cellist and conductor who founded the Barcelona Orchestra.

QUIZ
5

3   In a University building, what is the SCR?

4   What type of animal is a markhor?

5   Which international TV quiz has been hosted by Henry Kelly?

3   With reference to records, what did EP mean?

4   What type of animal is a Papillon?

5   In which TV competition are contestants required to use a flight simulator?

ROUND 5   *Individual questions for team 1*

The Bible
Name the fifth book of the Old Testament?

Words
Balm, dill and sorrel are all what?

Literature
Whose first novel was *This Sporting Life*?

History
Who was Mary Queen of Scots' first husband?

Sport
Name the youngest-ever World Heavyweight Champion.

Team 2

Team 1

ROUND 6

1   On which Canadian river is London, Ontario?

2   In the 1960s, who was the London osteopath who committed suicide at the height of the Christine Keeler affair?

3   Which pop group was originally called High Numbers?

1   Cairo and Memphis are on which American river?

2   In the 1960s, whose Report had a far-reaching effect on British travel?

3   Which heavy metal group starred in the film, *The Song Remains the Same*?

4 Who were the stars of the 1945 film, *The Lost Weekend*?

5 In the *Forsyte Saga*, who was Irene's second husband?

4 Who were the starts of the 1937 film, *Lost Horizon*?

5 Who was 'The Merchant of Venice'

ROUND 7

1 In which country is Kvass a traditional drink?

2 Which English city was called 'Luguvalium' by the Romans?

3 What was the name, meaning Minority Members, of the moderate socialist party in Russia, which was suppressed in 1922?

4 What is the main town on the Isle of Sheppey?

5 In which year did the Boston Tea Party take place?

1 In which country is the Barossa Valley Vineyard?

2 Which English city was called 'Durovernum' by the Romans?

3 Of which tribe was Boadicea the Queen?

4 Which thoroughfare on Manhattan Island is the centre of New York advertising?

5 In which year did *RMS Queen Elizabeth* make her first commercial voyage?

ROUND 8

1 Which oratorio by Elgar takes a poem by Cardinal Newman as its text?

2 In the 1960s, in which country was Ben Bella overthrown?

3 What does it mean when a drink is served 'frappé'?

1 Which nickname links a Beethoven piano concerto and a Strauss waltz?

2 In the 1960s, what way of detection was first used by Scotland Yard?

3 What do Americans call 'jam'?

4 In which year were the first Winter Olympic Games held?

5 In what sport was Larry Mahan All Round Champion from 1966 to 1970, and again in 1973?

4 On which Saint's Day was the Battle of Agincourt fought?

5 Who was Britains' lead-off man in Tokyo, 1991, when they won the 4 × 400 m Relay World Title?

ROUND 9

1 In which language is *Stern* magazine published?

2 Of what was Edward Kennedy convicted in the Chappaquiddick incident?

3 Which Island group used to be called the Spice Islands?

4 Who was nicknamed 'the Liberator'?

5 What instrument did Franz Liszt play?

1 Which country's alphabet has the most letters?

2 Who was the only American President to have been impeached?

3 Which ancient city, abandoned in 1434, was the capital of the Khmer Empire?

4 Who was nicknamed 'K of K'?

5 What instrument did Sarasate play?

ROUND 10 *Individual questions for team 2*

The Bible
Which city in Turkey was the birth place of St Paul?

Words
If you were studying 'Coleoptera' what would you be examining?

Literature
Who won the Booker Prize in 1981, for *Midnight's Children*?

History
In Mediaeval times there were three kinds of guild. Crafts and religious were two; what was the third?

Sport

Who won the Amateur Grand Slam of Tennis in 1962 and the Open Grand Slam in 1969?

Team 1   **Team 2**

DRINKS ROUND

1 In World War II, what were 'paravanes' used for?

1 What name is given to the knife of the Gurkha soldiers?

2 Who was the first leader and vocalist of the Crickets?

2 Who first sang about a dedicated follower of fashion?

3 Name one of Chekhov's 'Three Sisters'.

3 In *Vanity Fair*, who marries Rawdon Crawley?

4 At which American university were four students shot dead by National Guardsmen in May 1970?

4 In the late 1970s, the country house of Lord Rosebery was sold. What was it called?

5 The island group formerly called the New Hebrides is now known as which country?

5 Which West Indian island is occupied by the Dominican Republic and Haiti?

6 Which international Rugby Union side is nicknamed 'The Pumas'?

7 Which international Rugby Union side is nicknamed 'The Eagles'?

7 What was the surname of the TV Western hero 'Cheyenne'?

7 In which 1950s TV series did Broderick Crawford say 'Ten Four'?

8 Of which opera is Captain Macheath the hero?

8 In which Puccini opera is the hero shot, the villain stabbed and the heroine commits suicide?

9 Name the British airship which crashed in France on its first flight to India killing 48 people.

9 Who designed the R100 airship?

10 RA are the international car registration letters for which country?

10 T is the international car registration letter for which country?

RESERVE QUESTIONS
1 What is 'Nine Men's Morris'?
2 Which Greek playwright, according to legend, died after being hit on the head by a tortoise dropped by an eagle?
3 Which animal's fur is called 'nutria'?

Pub League Quiz 6

The individual questions are in Rounds 5 and 10 and are on the following subjects: Sport, French phrases, Opera, Literature and Which year?.

Team 1

Team 2

ROUND 1

1 What is the width of a hockey goal?
2 What is a 'Suffolk punch'?
3 St Helena was converted to Christianity by her son. Who was he?
4 From which book was the musical, *Half a Sixpence* adapted?
5 Which is the largest island of the West Indies?

1 What is the diameter of a basketball ring?
2 What is a 'scaup'?
3 Who is the patron saint of cripples and lepers?
4 From which book was the musical, *Hello Dolly* adapted?
5 Which is the largest of the Mediterranean islands?

ROUND 2

1 What is the product of the rattan palm used in furniture?
2 Who played 'Grasshopper' in TV's *Kung Fu*?
3 Who was Secretary General of the UN during the Cuban Missile Crisis?
4 What do Americans call Draughts?

1 Is the bathroom loofah animal, vegetable or mineral?
2 Who starred opposite Victoria Tennant in the TV epic *The Winds of War*?
3 Who was the first Secretary General of the UN?
4 In Monopoly, what is the colour of Bond Street?

5 How many masts does a sloop have?

5 What colour light is displayed on the starboard side of a ship?

ROUND 3

1 What do Glastonbury, ladderback and fauteuil have in common?

2 By what other name is the constellation Pyxis known?

3 Which well known tune from Bach's *Suite No. 3 in D* was transcribed for the lowest string on the violin?

4 Which Italian sauce is made with basil, garlic oil and pine kernels?

5 In which TV play, by Alan Bennett, did Coral Browne play herself?

1 What do St Gotthard, Lotschberg, Cascade and Moffat have in common?

2 In which constellation is the Pole Star?

3 What is the popular name of Chopin's *Prelude No. 15 in D Flat, Opus 28*?

4 'Borsch' or 'bortsch' is a soup from Russian and Poland. From what it is made?

5 Who was the first presenter of *Monitor*, who went on to become Director General of the BBC?

ROUND 4

1 What significance did the number 49 have for James Knox Polk?

2 What name is given to the smallest of the mosses?

3 In which 18th century book do we first meet the Yahoos?

1 On what kind of plane was Lyndon Johnson sworn in?

2 What is the largest agricultural crop by weight of the USA?

3 Which Hemingway novel is set in the Spanish Civil War?

4 How is the American Tennis player, Hazel Hotchkiss, now remembered?

5 In the Old Testament, Esau sold his birthright. To whom?

4 Which horse racing institution was founded in 1916 by Col. Hall-Walker (later Lord Wavertree)?

5 In which village did Jesus turn water into wine?

ROUND 5   *Individual questions for team 1*

Sport
In cricket we call them 'Extra's; what do the Australians call them?

French phrases
What does '*tout de suite*' mean?

Opera
Which Italian composer wrote the opera *Turandot*?

Literature
Who wrote *Morte d'Arthur*, printed by Caxton in 1485?

Which year?
In which year did Richard Nixon resign as President of the USA?

Team 2

Team 1

ROUND 6

1 Which American dancer died when her scarf caught in the rear wheel of a friend's car in Nice in 1927?

2 Which architect was engaged by James I to design scenery for masques and plays?

1 Which British author died of typhoid in Paris in 1931, after drinking the local water to show that it was safe?

2 Who designed the Brighton Pavilion?

3 Which Lloyd Webber show followed *Jesus Christ Superstar*?

4 What, to the nearest degree, is Absolute Zero in the Celsius scale?

5 Who wrote the words of 'Jerusalem'?

ROUND 7

1 What is the date of Twelfth Night?

2 In which country is Tobruk, the scene of heavy fighting during WWII?

3 In 1963, which American island prison closed?

4 In which 1959 film did Peter Sellers play a militant shop steward?

5 Who wrote the play *The Second Mrs Tanqueray*?

ROUND 8

1 Where in Britain would you find the Wallace Monument?

2 Who composed *The Walk to the Paradise Garden*?

3 N is the civil aircraft

3 Which 1971 musical saw David Essex as Jesus Christ?

4 What unit of heat will raise the temperature of 1 gram of water by one degree Celsius?

5 Who wrote the words of 'Auld Lang Syne'?

1 What is the date of St David's Day?

2 In which country was Lidice, the village destroyed by Nazis in 1942?

3 What was banned from British TV screens in August 1965?

4 In which 1938 Hitchcock film does Miss Froy write her name on a steamed-up train window?

5 Who wrote the play *An Inspector Calls*?

1 Where in Britain would you find the Monument marking where Prince Charles Edward raised his standard in August 1745?

2 Who composed *Clair de Lune*?

3 OO is the civil aircraft

marking for which country?

4 In which TV series did Paul Shane play a family butler?

5 Of which present day country was Gnaeus Julius Agricola governor in the first century AD?

marking for which country?

4 In which TV series did Ian McShane play a shady antiques dealer?

5 Who was the first Christian Roman Emperor?

ROUND 9

1 Which character in *The Jungle Book* film owed his voice to Phil Harris?

2 Which animal has earned the nickname 'Glutton'?

3 Which group had a hit in 1967 with 'Seven Rooms of Gloom'?

4 Who were the victims of the St Bartholomew's Day Massacre of 1572?

5 Who, in a poem, wrote 'Come friendly bombs and fall on Slough'?

1 Who was Roger Rabbit's wife?

2 Which present-day animal is thought to be the closest living relative of the extinct 'Quagga'?

3 What was the Village Peoples only No. 1 hit in Britain?

4 What name was given to the anti-Catholic riots of 1780?

5 Who wrote, in 1948, the novel *The Loved One*, which satirized Hollywood funeral customs?

ROUND 10   *Individual questions for team 2*

Sport
In Equestrian events, what is the literal meaning of 'dressage'?

French phrases
What does '*entre nous*' mean?

Opera
Which Italian composer wrote the opera *Aida*?

Literature
In *A Tale of Two Cities*, who kept a knitted tally of the names of her aristocratic victims?

Which year?
In which year was the Battle of Waterloo?

Team 1	Team 2

DRINKS ROUND

Team 1

1 In which European country did Ayatollah Khomeni spend his years of exile before returning to Iran?

2 As whom is Vincent Furnier better known in rock circles?

3 What was the name of the block of flats which collapsed in London in May 1968?

4 Which famous contralto worked as a switchboard operator before her rise to fame?

5 In 'The Ballard of John Axon', what kind of accident was commemorated?

6 Judge Jeffreys presided over the trials in 1685, following which rebellion?

Team 2

1 Who was India's first Prime Minister?

2 Who sang about 'The Green green grass of home'?

3 Where, in Wales, was the scene of the mining tip disaster of October 1966?

4 Which English tune is mentioned twice in *The Merry Wives of Windsor*?

5 Which London railway had the first driverless electric trains?

6 Who was the world's first qualified woman pilot?

7 What is the modern name for the ancient city of Edo?

7 Which Island is linked to Brooklyn by the Verrazano Narrows Bridge in New York?

8 Who in 1965 became the first foreigner in 45 years to win the American Open Golf title?

8 What is the only major golf tournament Arnold Palmer never won?

9 Who wrote *The Country Diary of an Edwardian Lady*?

9 Which renowned English author had been a Polish sailor in the French and British Merchant Service?

10 In musical terms what does *vivace* mean?

10 In musical terms what does *andante* mean?

RESERVE QUESTIONS

1 Who was President Ford's Vice President?
2 How many bits are there in a byte?
3 O is the chemical symbol for Oxygen. What is O_3? (said, Oh, three).

Pub League Quiz 7

The individual questions are in Rounds 5 and 10 and are on the following subjects: Television, Mythology, Literature, Words and Sport.

Team 1

Team 2

ROUND 1

1 What does RADA stand for?

2 To what animal does the adjective 'vulpine' refer?

3 The Rijks Museum in Amsterdam exhibits Rembrandt's famous painting, *The Night Watch*. What was revealed when it was cleaned?

4 In the Bible, who was the grandfather of Noah, and according to Genesis lived to the age of 969 years?

5 John George Haigh was hanged for murder in 1949. What method did he use to get rid of the bodies?

1 What does PLA stand for?

2 To which animals does the adjective 'porcine' refer?

3 Sir John Suckling was a poet and wit at the Court of Charles I. What did he invent?

4 Simon, called Peter, with his brother were both disciples and followers of Christ. What was Simon's brother's name?

5 Who, according to tradition, murdered several wives in turn because they showed undue curiosity about a locked room?

ROUND 2

1 Which musical was originally due to be entitled 'Welcome to Britain'?

1 Which Hitchcock film of 1934 did he remake in 1956?

2 In Troy weight, how many grains make a pennyweight?

3 In 1431, which English king was crowned King of Paris?

4 Which baseball fielding position is behind home plate?

5 French kings used to be crowned in the cathedral of which city?

2 What would a Dines Tilting Syphon measure?

3 Which English king, in the play by Christopher Marlowe, was murdered with a red-hot poker?

4 Which sport do you associate with the Talbot and the Waterloo Handicaps?

5 What is the city now called, that the Romans called Lutetia?

ROUND 3

1 Which couple recorded 'At the Drop of a Hat'?

2 Who wrote the novel *The Bridges at Toko-Ri*?

3 In which country are the Swabian Alps?

4 To which flower family does the pimpernel belong?

5 Who wrote the music for *Les Sylphides*?

1 Who has played Phil Archer on radio for over 40 years?

2 Who wrote *Kes*?

3 In which country are the Cantabrian Mountains?

4 Which plant is also called 'Elephant's Ears'?

5 Who composed *Sinfonia Antarctica* in 1953?

ROUND 4

1 What is the collective word for a group of larks?

2 In which English county is Goole?

3 Which poet was MP for Hull for 20 years, and wrote 'To His Coy Mistress?'

1 What is the collective term for a group of magpies?

2 In which English county is Guisborough?

3 Who wrote the poem 'Rape of the Lock'?

| 4 What do you measure with a Hygrometer? | 4 What do you measure with a Bolometer? |
| 5 With whom does Michael Jackson sing on the single 'State of Shock'? | 5 Who sang with Michael Jackson on 'The Girl is Mine'? |

ROUND 5 *Individual questions for team 1*

Television
On which programme did the Beatles make their first TV appearance in 1962?

Mythology
According to Greek mythology, what was Charon's employment?

Literature
What author created characters Gabriel Oak, Jude Fawley and Angel Clare?

Words
What was a 'tocsin'?

Sport
Who resigned as manager of Liverpool F.C. in February 1991?

| Team 2 | Team 1 |

ROUND 6

1 Which city does Haneda International Airport serve?	1 Which American city does McCarran Airport serve?
2 Which actress was known as the 'Queen of the Swashbucklers'?	2 What was 'Skip' Homeier's given name?
3 In Greek mythology, who is both sister and wife to Zeus?	3 Who was the Roman Goddess who equated with the Greek Hera?
4 Which European	4 Which European

capital city stands on an Island called Zealand?

5 At what boxing weight was Archie Moore World Champion?

capital city's name means 'Danish town'?

5 At which two weights was Terry McGovern world boxing champion?

ROUND 7

1 Which book of the Old Testament precedes Deuteronomy?

2 Peter the Hermit lived between 1050 and 1115. For what was he known historically?

3 Who is the Patron Saint of Spinsters?

4 What sort of creature is a sandpiper?

5 Which great cricketer equalled the world record for the long jump?

1 Which book of the New Testament precedes 1 Corinthians?

2 Who was the Italian secretary of Mary Queen of Scots, who was assassinated in front of the Queen in 1566?

3 Which Quarter Day was known as Pack-rag Day?

4 What sort of creature is a cayman?

5 Which great cricketer crossed the Alps accompanied by elephants?

ROUND 8

1 Brontophobia is a fear of what?

2 Which river 68 miles in length, is the longest wholly within Wales?

3 In which country is the Bay of Pigs?

4 What does a petrologist study?

5 Which soccer team plays home matches at Ewood Park?

1 Clinophobia is a fear of what?

2 Stirling is sited on which river?

3 In which country is Monopoli?

4 What does a pedologist study?

5 Which soccer team plays home matches at Portman Road?

QUIZ 7

ROUND 9

1 Which knight and actor provides the voice of Paddington Bear?

2 Which bird is called a Mavis?

3 Whose first novel was *Hatter's Castle* and first play, *Jupiter Laughs*?

4 The Brazilian spirit, Tiquira, is made from which roots?

5 Who, helped by his sons, made the famous violins of Cremona?

1 Which comedian was Headmaster of St Michael's?

2 Every dog has his day, every man his – what?

3 Whose first novel was *The Loving Spirit*, and autobiography *Growing Pains*?

4 From what is Rum distilled?

5 Who wrote the *Hammerklavier Sonata*?

ROUND 10 *Individual questions for team 2*

Television
The finals of which boardgame World Championship were shown on TV in November 1991?

Mythology
In mythology, what was the only animal that could kill a basilisk?

Literature
Who wrote '*Lucky Jim*'?

Words
What is a 'pedagogue'?

Sport
Who was the first woman in the 1989 London Marathon?

Team 1	*Team 2*

DRINKS ROUND

1 In which State of the USA is the Liberty Bell to be seen?

1 Famed in the song, in which State of the USA is Tulsa?

2 Who was the author, in 1976, of *Ross: story of a shared life*?

3 Which Egyptian caused the Great Pyramid of Cheops to be built?

4 What bone has the medical name 'sternum'?

5 Which County Cricket Club's badge depicts a daffodil?

6 Who had a hit with 'You Spin me Round' in 1985?

7 Who were Mrs Ford and Mrs Page?

8 Which country has sovereignty over Bouvet Island in the South Atlantic?

9 If you were anosmic, what would be wrong with you?

10 Which comedian once presented *It's A Square World* on TV?

2 Who was the author, in 1976, of *William McGonagal, the truth at last*?

3 Which Egyptian King was ousted in 1952?

4 How many fused bones form the coccyx?

5 Which county did Bob Willis play for?

6 Who had a hit with 'Goody Two Shoes'?

7 Which legendary king's sister was Morgan le Fay?

8 In which Bay are the Belcher Islands?

9 What does a funambulist do?

10 Who used to ask the questions in *The Sky's The Limit*?

RESERVE QUESTIONS

1 Which TV company's base was nicknamed 'Eggcup Towers'?

2 Name the Penlee lifeboat lost, just before Christmas, 1981, with all hands?

3 Who wrote the six *Sun Quartets*, so called from the first publishers trade-mark?

Pub League Quiz 8

The individual questions are in Rounds 5 and 10 and are on the following subjects: Quotations, Plants, Poetry, Ships and the Sea and Television.

Team 1

Team 2

ROUND 1

Team 1

1 Against which King did Hereward the Wake rebel?

2 What sort of creature is a sewin?

3 How long is a standard Olympic rowing course?

4 Which country in South America was called Banda Oriental before Independence?

5 Who won her first Oscar for the film *Klute*, in 1971?

Team 2

1 Against which King was a plot hatched by George Brooke and Lord Cobham, his brother?

2 What type of creature is a brandling?

3 In which year did the first (recorded) women's cricket match take place?

4 In which country is the Anti-Lebanon mountain range?

5 Which ex TV-cop won an Oscar for *Chariots of Fire*?

ROUND 2

Team 1

1 Which instrument does the 'hardangerfele' closely resemble?

2 Who wrote *Crime and Punishment*?

3 Which artist did a series of etchings called *The Disasters of War*?

Team 2

1 Which Indian, long-necked musical instrument has seven strings?

2 Who wrote of a doctor's rise to Harley Street in *The Citadel*?

3 Which artist painted *The Fighting Temeraire*?

4 What would a myologist study?

5 What was Che Guevara's given name?

4 What does a Somatologist study?

5 Which country was once ruled by Boleslaw the Generous?

ROUND 3

1 According to the saying, 'A swarm of bees in June' is worth – what?

2 Of what is nyctophobia the fear?

3 Manama is the capital of which country?

4 What would you put in a Canterbury?

5 Who wrote the play *John Bull's Other Island*?

1 According to the saying, 'Button to the chin' till – ' what?

2 Of what is gymnophobia the fear?

3 Harare is the capital of which country?

4 For what is a Davenport intended?

5 Who wrote the play *The Lady's not for Burning*?

ROUND 4

1 In Apothecaries' Weight, how many grains make a scruple?

2 What in World War II were 'Talboys' and 'Grand Slams'?

3 Which is the only case in British history of a husband and wife ruling jointly as King and Queen?

4 Who made the 1964 top-selling record, 'I Love You Because'?

5 What is 505, in Roman numerals?

1 According to Tennyson, the Light Brigade charged for half a league. How far is a league?

2 What kind of aircraft was the World War II 'Horsa'?

3 Which French King did Joan of Arc assist to defeat the English?

4 Whose first No. 1 hit was 'Release Me'?

5 Which year uses all the Roman numerals in descending order?

ROUND 5 *Individual questions for team 1*

Quotations
Who wrote, 'Cauliflower is nothing but cabbage with a college education'?

Plants
What flower is sometimes known as the 'Lent lily'?

Poetry
Which Scottish poet was known as the Ettrick Shepherd?

Ships and the Sea
What in shipping terms is a VLCC?

Television
In the TV play *Squaring the Circle*, which political leader was played by Bernard Hill?

Team 2	Team 1

ROUND 6

Team 2	Team 1
1 How many players are there in a netball team?	1 How high is the netball net from the ground?
2 According to the old saying, which fruit is it unlucky to eat in October?	2 'Edible', 'hazel' and 'squirrel-tailed' are kinds of what?
3 In which Kings' reign did the Pensionary Parliament assemble?	3 Which King won the Battle of the Spurs?
4 What sort of music did Ira D. Sankey compose?	4 For singing what type of music was Mahalia Jackson renowned?
5 Who wrote 'The Hollow Men'?	5 Who wrote *Fitz-Boodle's Confessions and Professions*?

ROUND 7

Team 2	Team 1
1 Which periodical was first published in 1902	1 Which former editor of *The Times* became

and edited by Bruce Richmond?

2 Who, in the 1960s, had a hit with 'I was Kaiser Bill's Batman'?

3 How many square metres are there in a hectare?

4 What is a layer of oysters called?

5 Which Italian city's symbol is the Winged Lion of St Mark?

ROUND 8

1 Who wrote the book *One Hundred and One Dalmatians*?

2 In which sport would you use the terms: 'Spike', 'Dump', 'Dig pass' and 'Penetration'?

3 What would you have if you had a 'Dandie Dinmont'?

4 In the history of the British Regiments, for what did KOSB stand for?

5 Which Biblical character in the book of Samuel was born in Gath?

chairman of the Arts Council?

2 Who had a hit in 1968 with 'Tiptoe Through the Tulips'?

3 What is the minimum number of whole degrees in a reflex angle?

4 Which seaport in Kent has been noted for its oysters since pre-Roman times?

5 In which city is the Palace of the Nations?

1 Who wrote *Thomas the Tank Engine*?

2 What, in sport, is a 'Karateka'?

3 Who or what is a 'blue faced booby'?

4 What do the initials TAVR stand for?

5 What collective name is given to the three wise men of the East?

ROUND 9

1 Where in your body would you find your adenoids?

2 What is the lowest prime number?

3 In Hindu mythology, what is an 'Avatar'?

4 'The Impossible Dream' comes from which musical?

5 Joe Lynch and John Bluthal starred together in which TV series?

1 Lentigines is the medical term for what?

2 What is the lowest perfect number?

3 Who was the Greek God of Fault-finding?

4 Which musical is a fantasy about a dead man returning after 15 years to help his family?

5 In which year was the *Cheers* bar established.

ROUND 10   *Individual questions for team 2*

Quotations
Who wrote, 'If in doubt, win the trick'?

Plants
By what name are the flower trusses of the hazel and willow trees known?

Poetry
Who had an 'ancient, trusty, drouthy, crony' named Souter Johnny?

Ships and the Sea
Name the legendary spectral ship condemned to sail the seas forever, trying to reach Table Bay?

Television
What does ORACLE stand for (exactly)?

Team 1	*Team 2*

DRINKS ROUND

1 Who wrote the song 'Camptown Races'?

1 Who wrote the hymn 'Abide with Me'?

2 In which country is Nagoya?

3 In which year did the Great Train Robbery take place?

4 Systolic and diastolic are the upper and lower values of what?

5 What was the codename for the Battle of Alamein?

6 The Prime Minister lives at No. 10 Downing Street, the Chancellor at No. 11; who lives at No. 12?

7 On which river is Caldron Snout on the Durham/Cumbria border?

8 Who played the part of 'Spider Man'?

9 Which sport is played at Cowdray Park?

10 Tocophobia is a fear of what?

2 In which country is Pau?

3 In which year was the first human heart transplant?

4 Name the tubes connecting the nose and ears?

5 What was the codename for the German invasion of The Soviet Union in 1941?

6 Which Prime Minister was nicknamed 'Pam'?

7 By what name is the Thames known as it flows through Oxford?

8 Which actor did his own stunts when playing the lead in the film *Condorman*?

9 Major Ernst Killander is known as the 'Father' of which sport?

10 Sitophobia is a fear of what?

RESERVE QUESTIONS
1 Where is the Headquarters of OPEC?
2 Who produced the Camargue car?
3 In which Shipping Forecast Area is Bell Rock Lighthouse?

Pub League Quiz 9

The individual questions are in Rounds 5 and 10 and are on the following subjects: Animals, USA, Science, Television and Plays.

Team 1	**Team 2**

ROUND 1

1 In which European country are the Cantabrian Mountains?

1 In which African country are the Aberdare Mountains?

2 Who was the husband of Boadicea?

2 Who was the husband of Philippa of Hainault?

3 What was Mickey Mouse's original name?

3 What is Princess Aurora's better-known name?

4 Which famous African battle took place in 1898?

4 Which famous English battle took place in 1644?

5 Who wrote 'The Bab Ballads'?

5 Who wrote the 'Piers Plowman' poems?

ROUND 2

1 What is alliteration?

1 What is litotes?

2 What did the Education Act of 1944 do?

2 What did the Toleration Act of 1689 do?

3 In which country would you use the currency Balboa?

3 In which country would you use the currency Gourde?

4 Who was British Prime Minister between 1916 and 1922?

4 Who first became Prime Minister in 1868?

5 What shape are the 'boxes' on the Blockbusters board?

5 Which game show was derived from Hollywood Squares?

ROUND 3

1 For which blind English composer did Eric Fenby write down the music?

1 What pseudonym was used by the English composer Philip Heseltine?

2 Tabasco is a kind of sauce, but in which country is Tabasco?

2 In which country is Spa?

3 What type of amphibians are the 'crested' and the 'palmated', both of which are native to Britain?

3 Which fish is known as the 'River Wolf'?

4 Which 1963 film starring Tom Courtenay, featured the undertakers, Shadrack & Duxbury?

4 John Wayne won an Oscar for playing which one-eyed Marshal?

5 Which island did Britain cede to Germany in 1890?

5 What did Britain get in exchange for this ceded island?

ROUND 4

1 What has been called the Universal Solvent?

1 Diamond is one of the crystalline forms of carbon. What is the other?

2 Which English poet, born in 1793, became insane in 1837 and died in an asylum in 1864?

2 Which American poet entitled a poem, 'Happiness makes up in height for what it lacks in length'?

3 Which two South American countries do not border Brazil?

3 Which two countries have permanent settlements on Spitsbergen?

4 Who was the creator of TV's *Potty Time*?

4 Who was 5C's teacher in *Please Sir*?

5 What is the common term for the tympanic membrane?

5 What is a dactylogram?

Animals
If an animal is described as 'Pinniped', what does it have?

USA
Which became the 49th State of the USA on 3rd January 1959?

Science
Which acid is called vitriol?

Television
For which department did Bergerac work?

Plays
What is the theme of a Passion Play?

Team 2 | **Team 1**

ROUND 6

1 Where would you find a Crossjack, a Spanker and a Royal?

1 What is a Skua?

2 In 1958, who had a No. 1 hit with his own song, 'Diana'?

2 In 1967, who had their first British chart entry with 'New York Mining Disaster 1941'?

3 If you cook pasta 'al dente' what does it mean?

3 Which blue-veined cheese is named after a small town near Milan?

4 What is the name of the warship which sank on its maiden voyage in 1628 and is now restored in Stockholm?

4 What were the '*Clermont*' and the '*Comet*'?

5 Which actress starred opposite Humphrey

5 Which actress starred opposite Humphrey

QUIZ 9

62

Bogart in *To Have and Have Not*?

Bogart in *Sabrina*?

ROUND 7

1 Who won the 1984 Booker Prize for *Hotel du Lac*?

2 Who owned the 1981 Derby winner?

3 Meshed, Tabriz and Abadan are among the chief towns of which country?

4 In which TV series did a female, ex Senior Partner, expire in the lift shaft?

5 'Byzantine', 'Baroque' and 'Brutalism' are all what?

1 Who won the 1980 Booker Prize for *Rites of Passage*?

2 Who owned the 1968 Greyhound Derby winner, 'Camira Flash'?

3 Elbasan, Tiranë and Shkodër are the chief towns of which country?

4 Who, in a TV series, was the investigator attached to a west country radio station?

5 'Indian Runner', 'Muscovy' and 'Khaki Campbell' are all what?

ROUND 8

1 Who was the British author of the survey, *London Labour and the London Poor*?

2 In the 1987 film *Business as Usual*, in which kind of business does the story unfold?

3 Who wrote, 'Woman wants monogamy; Man delights in novelty.'?

4 Which is the most northerly capital in the world?

1 Which playwright's first volume of autobiography was entitled *A Better Class of Person*?

QUIZ 9

2 Which 1987 film told a story of Britain during World War II, as seen by a 9-year-old boy?

3 Who was the English political leader, who asked to be painted, 'warts and everything'?

4 Of which country is Belmopen the capital?

5 What event in May 1987 was a demonstration against unemployment?

5 In September 1986, who was enthroned as Archbishop of Capetown?

ROUND 9

1 What is French for 30?

2 Of which duchy was Charles the Bold the ruler?

3 What, in the publishing world, do the abbreviations CUP stand for?

4 What is the word for a person who sells ribbons, buttons, hooks, tape etc?

5 When did pound notes first come into circulation in England?

1 What is Italian for 40?

2 Of which country was Philip Augustus the ruler?

3 What do the abbreviations OUDS stand for?

4 What is the word for a person who studies elections and voting patterns?

5 In which year was the *Lusitania* sunk?

ROUND 10 *Individual questions for team 2*

Animals

What is the correct name for a kangeroo's pouch?

USA

Which American Vice-President resigned in 1973, in the face of criminal charges?

Science

What is made by infusing carbonic acid gas into water under pressure?

Television

Which actor played Rodney Trotter in *Only Fools and Horses*?

Plays

Which play by Ben Jonson has the alternative title *The Fox*?

Team 1	Team 2

DRINKS ROUND

Team 1

1 Which comedian uses the catch phrase 'Katanga'?

2 What is the common name for Scriveners' Palsy?

3 Which poem ends 'Fled is that music: Do I wake or sleep'?

4 Of whom did Lloyd George say, 'He saw foreign policy through the wrong end of a municipal drainpipe'?

5 What is the most southerly city ever to hold the Olympic Games?

6 Which music accompanied 'Hamlet' cigar TV ads?

7 The film *The Choirboys* was about which body of men?

8 In Greek mythology, who killed 'Ladon', the dragon of a hundred heads?

9 Which bird in days of old was known as the Laverock?

10 Which soccer team is nicknamed the 'Gulls'?

Team 2

1 Which comedian used to reminisce about 'The day war broke out'?

2 Which part of your body does the tragus protect?

3 Who wrote the patriotic poem 'Drake's Drum'?

4 Who said of Viscount Montgomery, 'In defeat unbeatable; in victory unbearable'?

5 What is the most northerly city ever to hold the Olympic Games?

6 What classical theme accompanied the 'Hovis' TV ads?

7 In which film does Laurence Olivier torture Dustin Hoffman by drilling into his teeth?

8 In Indian mythology, what is the earth supported by?

9 What is Britain's heaviest breeding bird?

10 Which soccer team is nicknamed the 'Potters'?

QUIZ
9

RESERVE QUESTIONS

1 Which European city does the airport of Tempelhof serve?
2 What was the name of Henry VIII's fool?
3 Why are 'bonfires' so called?

Pub League Quiz 10

The individual questions are in Rounds 5 and 10 and are on the following subjects: Sport, Geography, Literature, Pop music and Art.

Team 1 | **Team 2**

ROUND 1

Team 1

1 Which gulf lies between Sweden and Finland?
2 What colours are on the flag of the United Nations?
3 Who wrote the play, *Mourning becomes Electra*?
4 Who played Lady Dedlock in TV's *Bleak House*?
5 'On the Street Where You Live' comes from which musical?

Team 2

1 Which sea is between China and Korea?
2 What colour is a palomino horse?
3 Who wrote *The Playboy of the Western World*?
4 Who played the lead in TV's crime series, *Target*?
5 *The Matchmaker* became which musical?

ROUND 2

Team 1

1 Who murdered James I of Scotland?
2 In which country is the Orange River?
3 What are 'Feather', 'Fly', 'Running' and 'Herring Bone'?
4 Who defeated the Russians at the Battle of Tannenburg?
5 From which country does racing driver Nelson Piquet come?

Team 2

1 Who caused the murder of Edward II of England?
2 In which country is the Liffey River?
3 What is a 'Rigadoon'?
4 Whose fleet was defeated at the battle of Lepanto?
5 From which country does racing driver Keke Rosberg come?

QUIZ
10

67

ROUND 3

1 Of which country was Cetewayo once the ruler?

2 Which country manufactures the 'Saab' motor car?

3 Which poison was given to Socrates?

4 Who portrayed 'Edna the Inebriate Woman'?

5 Victor Barna was 15 times a world champion in which sport?

1 Henri Christophe was once the ruler of which country?

2 Which country manufactures the 'Buick' motor car?

3 Who was Ivanhoe's wife?

4 Who did Peter Ustinov portray in *Quo Vadis*?

5 Which sport do you associate with Ann Moore?

ROUND 4

1 In which county is Orford Castle?

2 Which King of England was nicknamed 'The Martyr'?

3 In the Bible, who were the Jebusites?

4 Which plant's name comes from the Greek for 'crane'?

5 Who wrote the opera *Elektra*?

1 In which county is St Mawes Castle?

2 Of which country was Henry the Navigator a prince?

3 In the Bible what were the Scribes?

4 Which flower's name means 'flesh colour'?

5 In which opera by Puccini do Ping, Pang and Pong appear?

QUIZ 10

ROUND 5 *Individual questions for team 1*

Sport
In which game might you use a 'cleek'?

Geography
The Azores belong to which country?

Literature
Who wrote *An Ideal Husband*?

Pop music
'I am a Woman' was written and sung by whom?

Art
Who painted *The Potato Eaters* and *Starry Night*?

Team 2	Team 1

ROUND 6

Team 2
1 Astigmatism relates to which organ of the body?
2 Which saint was a tax collector before becoming a disciple?
3 What nationality was the artist Juan Gris?
4 Which soccer team is nicknamed 'The Cottagers'?
5 Name the town featured in TV's *In the Heat of the Night*?

Team 1
1 Cystitis relates to which organ of the body?
2 Which saint was a disciple and a physician?
3 What nationality was the artist Henry Fuseli?
4 Gay Meadow is the home of which soccer team?
5 Who wrote the title music for TV's *In the Heat of the Night*?

ROUND 7

Team 2
1 In which country is the Great Slave Lake?
2 In 1833, Prince Otto of Bavaria became the first king of which country?
3 What were Mrs Beeton's given names?
4 Where is your occipital artery?
5 Which numbers flank '11' on a dartboard?

Team 1
1 In which country is Lake Torrens?
2 Which country did King Prakrama rule?
3 What was Nell Gwyn's given name?
4 Which is the largest nerve in the human body?
5 Which numbers flank '18' on a dartboard?

QUIZ
10

69

ROUND 8

1 Who wrote *Jude the Obscure*?
2 Which planet did Holst call 'The Mystic'?
3 On which race track was Jim Clark killed in 1967?
4 In which English city was Charles Dickens born?
5 Who starred in the 1971 film *Kotch*?

1 Who wrote *The Girls of Slender Means*?
2 Who composed the *Manfred Symphony* in 1885?
3 Who won the 1984 Monaco Grand Prix?
4 The Peterloo Massacre of 1819 occurred in which city?
5 Which actor starred as the submarine commander in *Operation Petticoat*?

ROUND 9

1 Who was Pot Black 1991 Champion?
2 In which Canadian province is Gander airport?
3 Which political party ruled India for the first 30 years of independence?
4 Who deals with Top Cat's misdemeanours?
5 'Emperor' and 'Rockhopper' are types of what?

1 Who held the Snooker World Championship for 20 years?
2 Logan International Airport serves which American city?
3 Which French politician was called 'The Tiger'?
4 Name the witch in *Willo the Wisp*.
5 What type of creature is a cottonmouth?

ROUND 10   *Individual questions for team 2*

Sport
By what name is the game 'Mintonette' now known?

Geography
In which Gulf is Anticosti Island?

Literature
Who wrote the novel *A Kind of Loving*?

Pop music
Which group made the L.P. 'All Around My Hat' in 1975?

Art
Who painted *Two Tahitian Women*?

Team 1   **Team 2**

DRINKS ROUND

	Team 1	Team 2
1	What relation was Lot to Abraham?	Which prophet denounced Ahab and Jezebel?
2	In Greek mythology, what did Charybdis form?	In Greek mythology, how many eyes had the giant Argus?
3	Who founded the British Union of Fascists?	Who founded the Zoological Society?
4	Who starred in the 1975 film *Dog Day Afternoon*?	Who was the male star of the 1966 film *Two For The Road*?
5	In the poem by Kipling, what was Gunga Din's job?	In 1892, Gentlemen Jim Corbett knocked out John L. Sullivan. What was remarkable about the fight?
6	In which sport might you perform a 'telemark'?	In which sport could you be given a 'mulligan'?
7	Which English county town used to be known as 'Dubris'?	In which English county are the Quantocks?

QUIZ
10

71

8 Who wrote the music for the show, *Carousel*?

9 Who reputedly haunts Hever Castle?

10 In which TV series did Bombadier Beaumont appear?

8 Who wrote the music for the show, *West Side Story*?

9 Which Queen is said to haunt Borthwick Castle?

10 For which company did TV's Reginald Perrin work?

RESERVE QUESTIONS
1 What is hydrogen's atomic number?
2 How many pence today would a crown be worth?
3 Who sings the theme song in the Bond film *Goldfinger*?

Pub League Quiz 11

The individual questions are in Rounds 5 and 10 and are on the following subjects: Geography, Animal world, Poetry, World of Plants and Television.

Team 1

Team 2

ROUND 1

1 Which British city is served by Aldergrove airport?
2 What would be measured using an anemometer?
3 In which sport is a 'piton' used?
4 The Yalu and Tumen Rivers mark the boundary between which two countries?
5 Who composed the song 'Falling in love with love'?

1 Which American city is served by O'Hare Airport?
2 What is a rheostat?
3 In which sport would you use a 'spoon' and a 'niblick'?
4 In which country is the River Xingu?
5 Who composed the song 'Over There'?

ROUND 2

1 What instrument did Sidonie Goossens play?
2 Name the two major Baseball leagues in the USA.
3 Which radio series made Arthur Askey's name in the late 1930s?
4 In which country is Quimper?

1 What instrument did Leon Goossens play?
2 Which club won the 1987 Rugby League Cup Final?
3 Who was radio's Diddy David?
4 In which country is Quatre Bras?

QUIZ
11

5 What, in the field of medicine, do the letters UCH stand for?

5 What, in the field of law, do the letters LJ stand for?

ROUND 3

1 What is the name for the heraldic colour red?

2 Who was 'The Doors' keyboard player?

3 'April is the cruellest month', starts which poem?

4 In which Welsh county is the Isle of Anglesey?

5 What does the phrase 'playing to the gallery' mean?

1 In heraldry, what is a Pale?

2 Who played the part of The Doors' keyboard player in the film *The Doors*?

3 Who wrote the poem 'The Waste Land'?

4 In which Welsh county is Brecknock?

5 What does the phrase 'drawing the long bow' mean?

ROUND 4

1 Who won the Silver Medal for the men's 800 metres in the 1984 Olympics?

2 Cholecystitis relates to which part of the body?

3 Who was the first Christian martyr?

4 What is the S.I. unit of measurement for frequency?

5 What nationality was Nobel Peace Prize Winner Lester B. Pearson?

1 How many times has Sebastian Coe won the Olympic 1500 m race?

2 Mastoiditis relate to which part of the body?

3 Which Pope had the longest reign?

4 What is the S.I. unit of measurement for electrical resistance?

5 What nationality was Nobel Chemistry Prize Winner Frederick Sanger?

ROUND 5 *Individual questions for team 1*

Geography
Of which European city is Piraeus the port?

Animal world
What kind of animal is a skink?

Poetry
If Tuesday's child is full of grace, what was Monday's child?

World of Plants
What is the common name for the plant Belladonna?

Television
Who was the third Dr Who?

Team 2	Team 1

ROUND 6

1 What is the capital of Morocco?

2 Spell ANAESTHETIC.

3 Sydney Carton dies at the end of which book?

4 Which pop group's single backed 'Knowing Me, Knowing You' with 'Happy Hawaii'?

5 In which country is Habsburg Castle?

1 What is the capital of Zaïre?

2 Spell CRUSTACEAN.

3 In which book does Maggie Tulliver feature?

4 Which pop group had a hit with 'Honkey Tonk Women'?

5 In which country is Canossa Castle?

ROUND 7

1 What is the common name for 'Canis Lupus'?

2 Which English King suffered mental derangement in 1453?

3 The lack of which vitamin causes beriberi?

1 What is the common name for 'Pongo pygmaeus'?

2 Which Queen was called 'Gloriana'?

3 The lack of which vitamin causes scurvy?

4 What is Viv Richard's first given name?

5 When Sherlock Holmes retired, what did he become?

ROUND 8

1 William Mitchell was which actor's real name?

2 At which battle did the Black Prince win his spurs?

3 To what family does the Jackdaw belong?

4 Who wrote the play *The Little Foxes*?

5 What was Cher's real name?

ROUND 9

1 In which country is the Maranon River?

2 In the Bible, what was a publican's job?

3 Which footballer was with three World Cup winning teams?

4 Who preceded Creon as King of Thebes?

5 Which musical note is known as '*double-croche*' in France?

3 What is Colin Cowdrey's first given name?

5 What was the name of Sherlock Holmes's brother?

1 Ruby Stevens was which actress's real name?

2 At which battle did Henry V fight in 1403 at the age 15?

3 What is an Ormer?

4 Who wrote the play *The Cocktail Party*?

5 What was Sonny's real name?

1 In which country is the Menderes River?

2 Which prophet's Lamentations are a book of the Old Testament?

3 Which athlete won three gold medals in the 1952 Olympics?

4 Which Libyan King did Col. Gaddafi overthrow in 1969?

5 Which note is four times the length of a crotchet?

QUIZ
11

76

ROUND 10 *Individual questions for team 2*

Geography
What is the capital of Puerto Rico?

Animal world
What creature takes the following forms during its life: 'parr', 'smolt' and 'grilse'?

Poetry
Which poet wrote the line 'You're a better man than I am, Gunga Din'?

World of Plants
The Whortleberry or Whimberry are other names for which wild fruit?

Television
What was the first product advertised on TV in 1955?

Team 1	Team 2

DRINKS ROUND

1 Who composed the *Death and the Maiden Quartet*?

2 Who was the husband of Mary II of England, Scotland and Ireland?

3 In which country is Meerut?

4 If, on January 1st, the time in London is 12.00 noon, what time is it in Delhi?

5 The Hospitals' Cup is competed for in which sport?

6 Who played the title role in the 1972 film *Young Winston*?

1 Who composed the *Tristesse Etude*?

2 Who was the husband of Berengaria of Navarre?

3 In which State of the USA is Bretton Woods?

4 If, on January 1st, the time in London is 12.00 noon what time is it in Tokyo?

5 In Karate, what does 'Tamashiwara' mean?

6 Who played the title role in the 1974 film *Big Bad Mama*?

QUIZ
11

77

7 What is a canvas back?

8 Name Shirley Williams' famous literary mother.

9 Which American State is known as the Hoosier State?

10 The American football team 'The Rams' come from where?

7 What is a zander?

8 Who was the leader of the Labour Party prior to Harold Wilson?

9 Which American State is known as the Old Dominion?

10 The American football team 'The Oilers' come from where?

RESERVE QUESTIONS

1 In which year did the Post Office introduce Christmas stamps?

2 Who composed the opera *Lohengrin*?

3 Who said 'Let me die with the Philistines'?

Pub League Quiz 12

The individual questions are in Rounds 5 and 10 and are on the following subjects: Places, Politics, Science, Words and Books.

Team 1	**Team 2**

ROUND 1

1	Who was nicknamed 'Toom Tabard'?	1	Who was nicknamed 'Prinny'?
2	What country is known in its native language as 'Hellas'?	2	Its inhabitants call it Kerkira; what do Britons call it?
3	What is the first section in an international ice skating competition?	3	Which ice skating event was first added to the 1976 Olympics?
4	In which novel does Lord Marchmain appear?	4	In which novel does Alfred Jingle appear?
5	Which Mafioso gangster was called 'Lucky'?	5	Which gangster was called 'Machine Gun'?

ROUND 2

1	Who painted *Rape of the Sabines* and *The Felt Hat*?	1	Which English portrait painter's subjects included Dr Johnson and Mrs Siddons.
2	In which city in the British Isles would you find Phoenix Park?	2	In which city in the British Isles would you find Cathay Park?
3	Who wrote more than 400 concertos for Venetian music schools for orphaned girls?	3	Which Spanish composer died in 1916, on board the torpedoed *Sussex*?
4	How far apart are the goal posts in polo?	4	How far is it between consecutive baseball bases?

5 On what date is 'Oak-apple Day'?

5 On what date is 'Holy Innocents' Day'?

ROUND 3

1 Which group had a hit with 'Blackberry Way'?

1 Which group had a hit with 'Blockbuster'?

2 Who wrote, 'Candy is dandy but Liquor is quicker'?

2 Who wrote, 'He who can, does. He who cannot, teaches'?

3 Who was the doubter among the apostles?

3 What was Jesus's first miracle?

4 In geology, what is a moraine?

4 In geology, what is loess?

5 Carson City is the capital of which American State?

5 New Orleans is in which American State?

ROUND 4

1 On which racecourse is the Cesarewitch run?

1 Which racecourse crosses the Melling Road?

2 Who wrote *The Black Tulip*?

2 Who wrote the verse-novel *Eugene Onegin*?

3 What instrument did Evelyn Rothwell play?

3 To which conductor was Evelyn Rothwell married?

4 Who was the last English King to have a Queen called Catherine?

4 Who was the first English King to obtain a divorce?

5 Which actress runs TV's *Bagdad Café*?

5 What is the name of the cab company in TV's *Taxi*?

ROUND 5 *Individual questions for team 1*

Places

For what is the town of Meissen, in Germany famous?

Politics

Which country's Parliament is known as the Knesset?

Science

With what is the science of cryogenics concerned?

Words

Who or what are 'Norns'?

Books

What would you find in *Debrett*?

Team 2	Team 1

ROUND 6

1 What nationality was Erasmus?

1 What nationality was Caractacus?

2 What instrument did Madame Suggia play?

2 What instrument did George Thalben-Ball play?

3 Who was the winning Commander at the battle of Tel-el-Kebir?

3 Who was the winning Commander at the naval battle of Camperdown?

4 How are showjumpers David Broome and Liz Edgar related?

4 Jill Parker was an English international on 413 occasions. What was her sport.

5 What is the State flower of California?

5 What is the State flower of Florida?

ROUND 7

1 Which civil war took place between 1936 and 1939?

1 Which mutiny took place in 1857 and 1858?

2 In which country is Cape Wrath?

2 Where is Cape Finisterre?

3 Who wrote the operetta *The Grand Duke*?

3 Who wrote the operetta that includes 'The Nuns' Chorus'?

4 In which Shakespeare play does a statue 'come to life'?

5 The first long-distance race was from Antwerp to London in 1819. Which sport?

4 In which Shakespeare play does Rosalind disguise herself as Ganymede?

5 Claire Tomlinson attained a handicap of five in 1986. Which sport?

ROUND 8

1 Who is the patron saint of Paris?

2 Which King had the nickname 'Lackland'?

3 What was the Latin name for Paris in Roman times?

4 Which S.I. unit is used to measure energy and quantity of heat?

5 Which group did Tom Rapp lead before going solo?

1 Who is the patron saint of Madrid?

2 Which King had the nickname 'Beauclerck'?

3 What was the Latin name for Cadiz in Roman times?

4 Which S.I. unit is used to measure quantity of electricity?

5 Which group was known as 'A.W.B.' for short?

ROUND 9

1 What does the French 'hors de combat' mean?

2 In which castle was King Edward the Martyr murdered in AD 978?

3 Which authoress also writes as Barbara McCorquodale?

4 What is 'Ogham'?

5 David Essex's hit number 'Oh What a Circus' came from which show?

1 What does the Latin 'locum tenens' mean?

2 Where was the first Prince of Wales proclaimed in 1301?

3 What was the name of Iran before it was called Persia?

4 What is 'Treen'?

5 Who was at No. 5 in the first British Top Ten, with 'High Noon'?

ROUND 10 *Individual questions for team 2*

Places
'Sing Sing' is located on the Hudson River. What is it?

Politics
In which country was the political party known as the 'Falangists'?

Science
What is Deuterium Oxide popularly called?

Words
What occupation does a 'coper' have?

Books
Who wrote 'Cautionary Tales'?

Team 1	Team 2

DRINKS ROUND

	Team 1		Team 2
1	Which motorway links the M25 to Folkestone?	1	Which motorway links the M25 to Cambridge?
2	In which country are the Ox Mountains?	2	In which country are the Adirondack Mountains?
3	Who ordered Lady Jane Grey to be executed?	3	The Prince of Saxe-Coburg-Gotha married which English Queen?
4	Who is Karol Wojtyla?	4	Who is Lord of the Isles?
5	Which cartoonist sent her characters to 'Tresoddit' in Cornwall?	5	In which newspaper would you find Posy Simmond's cartoons?
6	Leoprine refers to what type of animal?	6	What type of creature is a water moccasin?
7	Who sang 'I'd Like to Teach the World to Sing'?	7	Who sang 'I'm into Something Good'?

QUI? 12

8 In which country is the region of Andalusia?

9 Which city is the home of the Ajax club?

10 Who designed the fighter-bomber the 'Mosquito'?

8 In which country are the Pontine Marshes?

9 Which city is the home of the Benfica club?

10 Who designed the 'Spitfire'?

RESERVE QUESTIONS

1 In which book would you find the 'Slough of Despond'?

2 When is St Sylvester's night?

3 What is the sum total of all the trebles on a dart board?

Pub League Quiz 13

The individual questions are in Rounds 5 and 10 and are on the following subjects: Sport, Composers, History, Art and Poems.

Team 1

Team 2

ROUND 1

1 What, in the field of computers, does ASCII stand for?

2 Who wrote the novel *Fame is the Spur*?

3 Who was Cain's eldest son?

4 Whose second symphony was known as *The Little Russian*?

5 To which creature were the eyes of Argus transferred by Hera?

1 For what, in the field of aviation, do the letters ICAO stand?

2 Who wrote the novel *Scruples*?

3 What was Abel's occupation?

4 Who wrote the *Raindrop Prelude*?

5 What did the Greeks call 'The Pillars of Hercules'?

ROUND 2

1 Where in the British Isles would you find the House of Keys?

2 Where were the 1952 Summer Olympics held?

3 Who sang 'I heard it through the Grapevine'?

4 Which film ends with 'Rosebud' burning?

5 On which river does Leicester stand?

1 Where is the world's largest Fish and Chip shop?

2 Where were the 1968 Winter Olympics held?

3 Who sang 'King of the Road'?

4 In which film was 'Flubber' invented?

5 The Wirral lies between the Mersey and which other river?

QUIZ
13

ROUND 3

1 Of which country is Asuncion the capital city?
2 The international car registration letters FL come from where?
3 Which horse won the Derby, the 2000 Guineas and the St Leger in 1970?
4 Who wrote *The Woodlanders*?
5 'Lady's Slipper' is a variety of which flower?

1 What is the capital of the South American country Guyana?
2 The international car registration letters SK come from where?
3 Name the race-track where the Kentucky Derby is run.
4 Who wrote *Thérèse Raquin*?
5 Tobacco is made from the leaves of which family of plants?

ROUND 4

1 Who played 'Gloria' in *It Ain't Half Hot Mum*?
2 In which country is Latakia, famous for its tobacco?
3 Who would wear an 'Orphrey', a 'Morse' and a 'Cope'?
4 Who or what is a 'Cassowary'?
5 Where did Lee surrender to Grant in 1865?

1 Who is American TV's equivalent of Alf Garnett?
2 In which group of islands is Corfu?
3 What article of clothing are 'Domino', 'Cardinal' and 'Mantle'?
4 Who or what is a 'dragée'?
5 The 'February Revolution' led to the overthrow of which Republic of France.

ROUND 5   *Individual questions for team 1*

Sport
Which horse races for colts form the English Triple Crown?

Composers
Who composed *Eine Alpen-symphonie*?

History
What did the 'Volstead Act' in the USA seek to control?

Arts
Which famous painting by Millais shows the sea wall at Budleigh Salterton, Devon?

Poems
'White founts falling in the courts of the sun' is the first line of which poem?

Team 2	Team 1

ROUND 6

	Team 2		Team 1
1	Who wrote the thriller *The Five Red Herrings*?	1	Who wrote the book *The Wizard of Oz*?
2	Which King was buried at Westminster Abbey a few days after it was consecrated?	2	Who was the last English King to be killed in battle?
3	On which Island are the former British colonies of Sarawak and Brunei?	3	To which European country do the Island groups of Cyclades and Dodecanese belong?
4	Where in your body is the bone called the 'trapezium'?	4	Where is your 'sartorius muscle'?
5	In which sport is the Thomas Cup awarded?	5	From which country does snooker player Dene O'Kane come?

ROUND 7

	Team 2		Team 1
1	What is 8 in binary?	1	What is 4 in binary?
2	Which country did the League of Nations expel in December 1939 for attacking Finland?	2	Which warship was scuttled near Montevideo in December 1939.
3	In the Bible, who was the father of Ishmael?	3	Who was Moses father-in-law?

QUIZ
13

4 Which abstract impressionist became famous for his drip painting?

5 Which soccer team plays its home games at Hampden Park?

4 Who designed the Albert Memorial?

5 Which is the longest Olympic track race?

ROUND 8

1 Crown Prince Felipe is heir to which European throne?

2 On radio, Kenneth Williams was Sandy; who was Hugh Paddick?

3 What was Joe Gargery's trade in *Great Expectations*?

4 In which country could you spend the 'Cruzeiro'?

5 Which famous battle took place in 1415?

1 Crown Prince Frederick is heir to which European throne?

2 'Barwick Green' is the signature tune of which serial?

3 What was Silas Marner's trade, in the George Eliot novel?

4 In which country could you spend the 'Kwacha'?

5 Which famous English battle took place in 1264?

ROUND 9

1 Who wrote, 'Marriage has many pains, but celibacy has no pleasures'?

2 Queen Margrethe II became the first female sovereign for over 500 years of where?

3 FIM is the administering body of which sport?

1 Whose last words, on the scaffold, were 'Such is life'?

2 Of which country was Eric Bloodaxe king?

3 How much clearance does a croquet ball have, passing through a hoop?

QUIZ
13

4 What was the sequel to the 1933 film *King Kong*?

5 *Almaviva* was the original name of which Rossini opera?

4 What was the sequel to the film *Bedtime for Bonzo*?

5 Which Italian composer completed Puccini's opera *Turandot*?

ROUND 10 *Individual questions for team 2*

Sport
Which twins played cricket for Surrey in the 1950s?

Composers
Which composer pianist wrote the opera *Manru* in 1901?

History
Who was the husband of Madame de Maintenon?

Art
Who painted *Diana surprised by Actaeon* in 1559?

Poems
Who wrote the poem beginning 'Half a league, half a league'?

Team 1	Team 2

DRINKS ROUND

1 What was the earlier name of Tuvalu?

2 Whose first starring role was in the film *The Invisible Man* in 1933?

3 What is the positive square root of 289?

4 Which American President was architect of the Virginia State Capitol?

1 What was the earlier name of Zambia?

2 Who starred in *Modern Times* in 1936?

3 What is the positive square root of 441?

4 Who painted the *Rokeby Venus*?

QUI
13

5 Who created the imaginary place 'Narnia'?

5 Who wrote *Elmer Gantry*?

6 Whose mistress was reputedly the model for Britannia?

6 Who succeeded Henry VIII and at what age?

7 What is the capital of Lithuania?

7 Where is Kharg Island?

8 What sort of bird is a 'tercel'?

8 To which family of birds does the 'dabchick' belong?

9 In which sport do women compete for the Marcel Corbillon Trophy?

9 Which football club was founded, in 1895, as Thames Ironworks?

10 Who was Antigone's father?

10 Who was Eurydice's husband?

RESERVE QUESTIONS
1 Which Scottish 'Term Day' is on August 1st?
2 Who said, 'Life imitates art far more than art imitates life'?
3 Who had a hit record with 'Happiness'?

Pub League Quiz 14

The individual questions are in Rounds 5 and 10 and are on the following subjects: Television, Famous People, Pop music, History and Animals.

Team 1 *Team 2*

ROUND 1

1 Who composed 'Jesu, Joy of Man's Desiring'?

1 Who composed 'Country Gardens' and 'Handel in the Strand'?

2 In World War I, what were 'Little Willies' and 'Big Willies'?

2 Which German was given the unique rank of Reichsmarschall in World War II?

3 'Joanna the Mad' reigned which country in the 16th century?

3 'Charles the Bold', 1433–77, was the ruler of which country?

4 'Earth has not anything to show more fair' is from which poem?

4 'Deep in the shady sadness of a vale' is from which poem?

5 Name the retirement home in TV's *Waiting for God*?

5 Name one of the actors caught up in the TV's *Time Tunnel*.

ROUND 2

1 Who wrote the song 'Daisy Bell'?

1 Who wrote the song 'Days of Wine and Roses'?

2 What are the dimensions of a snooker table?

2 What are the dimensions of a table tennis table?

3 In which year was the Census introduced in Britain?

3 In which year was the two-tier postal system introduced in Britain?

4 Who recorded 'Below the Salt'?

4 Who sang 'Bad Moon Rising'?

5 On pencils, what does BBB mean?

5 On pencils, what does HB mean?

ROUND 3

1 Who were the two rival groups in the Battle of Blood River?

1 Between which two cities were the Punic Wars fought?

2 Who, in Greek mythology, turned Arachne into a spider?

2 In Greek mythology, Deucalion was the equivalent of whom in the Bible?

3 In which year did John Curry complete Ice Skating's Triple Crown?

3 In which year did Cassius Clay first win the World Heavyweight title?

4 Who viewed all of the Promised Land from Mount Nebo?

4 Who was Zipporah's husband?

5 Maseru is the capital of which country?

5 Niamey is the capital of which country?

ROUND 4

1 In Greek mythology, what was the Chimeira?

1 In Norse mythology, who wielded Mjölnir?

2 Who wrote the opera *Mozart and Salieri* in 1898?

2 Who wrote the opera *The Saint of Bleecker Street*?

3 Who painted *The Naked Maja*?

3 In the painting, who was 'The Naked Maja'?

4 Who was the Portuguese discoverer of Brazil?

4 Who was the European discoverer of the Mississippi River?

5 What are the two lifts used in Olympic Weightlifting?

5 Which sports are combined in an Olympic Biathlon?

ROUND 5   *Individual questions for team 1*

Television

In which London district is TV's *Only Fools and Horses* set?

Famous People
For what is Francis Scott Key best remembered?

Pop music
Whose hit album was called 'Dark Side of the Moon'?

History
Which King is it thought that Walter Tyrell killed in the year 1100?

Animals
What is a guanaco?

Team 2	Team 1

ROUND 6

	Team 2		Team 1
1	In science, what does RNA stand for?	1	In science, what does DNA stand for?
2	Who was the last Ottoman Sultan?	2	Who was the first Bourbon king of France?
3	Where is Cape Comorin?	3	Where is Queen Maud Land?
4	Who wrote *Staying On*?	4	Who wrote *The Battle of the Books*?
5	What was Beethoven's only Oratorio?	5	Who wrote the Coronation Anthem, *Zadok the Priest*?

ROUND 7

	Team 2		Team 1
1	Which film made Rudolph Valentino a star?	1	In which film did Fred Astaire sing 'Night and Day'?
2	For whom was the Taj Mahal built?	2	For whom is Big Ben named?
3	Who, in 1882, discovered the tuberculosis bacterium?	3	Who discovered radioactivity?
4	Which Rugby League player kicked 22 goals in a cup-tie?	4	Who was the oldest man to play Test Cricket?

5 What does Tokyo mean?

5 What was the former name of Tokyo?

ROUND 8

1 Name the two TV *Birds of a Feather*?

1 Name the leading character in TV's *So You Think You've Got Troubles*?

2 Where is the Denmark Strait?

2 Where is the Bay of Fundy?

3 Who created the character 'Peregrine Pickle'?

3 Who created the detective 'C. Auguste Dupin'?

4 Who composed the music to 'God Bless the Prince of Wales'?

4 Who composed the music to 'Deutschland Uber Alles'?

5 Where in the human body is the Brachial Artery?

5 Where in the human body is the Pineal Gland?

ROUND 9

1 In computer terminology what does PROM mean?

1 In computer terminology, for what is BASIC an acronym?

2 What 'first' reached Britain in July 1586?

2 What 'first' was introduced in Glasgow in October 1865?

3 Who wrote *A Day in the Death of Joe Egg*?

3 Who wrote *All Quiet on the Western Front*?

4 Who painted the *Madonna with the long neck*?

4 Who painted *Whaam*?

5 Who won both the UK and World Professional Billiards Champion-ships in 1987?

5 Which team won the Super Bowl in 1989?

ROUND 10 *Individual questions for team 2*

Television
Who played 'Haskins' in *The Sweeney*?

Famous People
What was Emperor Haile Selassie's original name?

Pop music
Who had a hit with 'I Feel for You' in 1985?

History
Which Ostrogoth was King of Italy from AD 493 to 526?

Animals
What is a kissing gourami?

Team 1	*Team 2*

DRINKS ROUND

1 Which countries fought the Chaco War?

2 What is a 'henry'?

3 What is the capital of Qatar?

4 Who stars in the film '*She'll be Wearing Pink Pyjamas*'?

5 What is a collection of crows called?

6 In Norse mythology, who caused Balder's death?

7 Which musician was portrayed in the film, *The Magic Bow*?

8 In which country is the Grande Dixence Dam?

1 Who fought whom at Taranaki in 1860?

2 What is a 'lux'?

3 What is the capital of Namibia?

4 Which famous actor starred in the melodrama, *The Bells*?

5 What is the collective term for bears?

6 In Greek mythology, who tried to fly to heaven on Pegasus?

7 Which composer was portrayed in the film, *A Song to Remember*?

8 In which country are the Guayra Falls?

QUIZ 14

9 Who compères the *Krypton Factor*?

9 Who played Baldrick in TV's *Blackadder*?

10 Who wrote the poems, 'Songs for St Cecilia's Day'?

10 Who wrote the poem 'Metroland'?

RESERVE QUESTIONS

1 In which city was Yehudi Menuhin born?
2 'North to the Future' is the motto of which American State?
3 What does STOLPORT stand for?

The Answers

Pub League Quiz 1 Answers

Team 1

Team 2

ROUND 1

1 Condensed milk.
2 Kathleen Mansfield.
3 Alan Autry.
4 Portugal's.
5 9.

1 The printing press.
2 Stevie Smith.
3 *The Lotus Eaters.*
4 Grace Darling.
5 28.

ROUND 2

1 Elton John and Kiki Dee.
2 Spanish.
3 The Duke of Wellington.
4 John Cleese.
5 The comma.

1 Leo Sayer.
2 Australia.
3 Viscount Melbourne.
4 *La Bamba.*
5 Z.

ROUND 3

1 An iron cannon (which burst in 1680 when firing a salute to Charles II).
2 Mount Fuji in Japan.
3 Gaston Leroux.
4 The Trojan War.
5 Benito Mussolini.

1 Edinburgh Castle.

2 Baltimore and Ohio.
3 Barker and Corbett.
4 A type of wine.
5 The Gestapo.

ROUND 4

1 South Africa.
2 A word that sounds the same as another but has a different meaning.
3 *The Red Badge of Courage.*
4 Swiss.
5 Earth.

1 Pakistan.
2 Exaggeration.

3 Tobias Smollett.
4 Russian.
5 Lodge.

ROUND 5

Abbreviations
Society for the Promotion of
Christian Knowledge.

Mythology
A Jackal.

Sport
6.

News of the 80s
York Minster.

United Kingdom
Lytham St Annes, Lancashire.

Team 2 | **Team 1**

ROUND 6

	Team 2		Team 1
1	Neil Simon.	1	Brendan Behan.
2	TH, for Talbot House.	2	'Tubby' Clayton.
3	1970.	3	1955.
4	The badger.	4	A monkey.
5	Corporal Klinger.	5	Miss Brahms.

ROUND 7

	Team 2		Team 1
1	Walpurgis Night.	1	May 1st.
2	20.	2	22.
3	St Francis of Assisi.	3	St Francis Xavier.
4	Zsa Zsa Gabor.	4	*The Sunday Correspondent.*
5	Azure.	5	Sable.

ROUND 8

	Team 2		Team 1
1	TSB (Trustee Savings Bank).	1	British Rail.
2	Polly James and Nerys Hughes.	2	Cyril Fletcher.
3	Above the taste or comprehension of ordinary people.	3	On active military service.
4	Sir William Walton.	4	Greig.
5	The Royal Corps of Transport.	5	The Royal Artillery.

ROUND 9

	Team 2		Team 1
1	55.	1	18.
2	The autogyro.	2	Concordski.
3	Albania.	3	Thailand.

4   Real tennis.
5   John McEnroe.

4   Rodeo.
5   Bob Champion.

ROUND 10

Abbreviations
Fellow of the Royal Society of Literature.

Mythology
7 young men and 7 young women to feed to the Minotaur.

Sport
Goal shooter and goal attack.

News of the 80s
Rosie Barnes.

United Kingdom
Belfast.

Team 1

Team 2

DRINKS ROUND

	Team 1		Team 2
1	The Black Sea.	1	The Atlantic.
2	Eric Clapton.	2	Roger Daltry.
3	Gamel Abdal Nasser.	3	Austria.
4	Noah's.	4	Alice Springs in Australia.
5	Grand Marnier.	5	Raspberry.
6	The cock.	6	Hawaii.
7	Jellystone National Park.	7	*Lady and the Tramp*.
8	Vesuvius.	8	Pontius Pilate.
9	Hieronymus Bosch.	9	The world's largest painting.
10	Kabaddi.	10	The clay pigeon trap.

RESERVE QUESTIONS
1   The USSR's Aeroflot.
2   The Bonzo Dog Do-dah Band.
3   Berlioz.

Pub League Quiz 2 Answers

Team 1

Team 2

ROUND 1
1   The *Turbinia*.

1   The *Fram*.

2 Wilkie Collins.
3 Fulchester.
4 Ecuador.
5 Linus Pauling.

2 Nicolas Freeling.
3 Walnut Grove.
4 India.
5 Economics.

ROUND 2

1 Chris de Burgh.
2 P.L. Travers.
3 The Leone.
4 W.T. Tilden.
5 Clodagh Rodgers.

1 Irene Cara.
2 Rudyard Kipling.
3 The Dinar.
4 Henry Armstrong.
5 Stevie Wonder.

ROUND 3

1 Niccolò Machiavelli.

1 Benjamin Disraeli (Earl of Beaconsfield).

2 Israel.
3 Richard Greene.

2 Poland.
3 *The Return of Doctor X.* (1939)

4 Andrew Jackson.
5 Skittles.

4 William McKinley.
5 Lacrosse.

ROUND 4

1 Florence.
2 Dr. Moreau (*The Island of Dr Moreau*, H.G. Wells).
3 Potassium nitrate.
4 Princess Margaret.

5 Edward Woodwood.

1 Benvenuto Cellini.
2 Dr Zhivago.

3 Magnesium sulphate.
4 Prince Andrew, Duke of York.
5 Richard Harris.

ROUND 5

Television
The Prisoner.

Sport
The Jockey Club.

Plants
Foxglove.

Religion
The Hindu religion.

Words
The dating of past events by analysis of tree rings.

Team 2	Team 1

ROUND 6

Team 2	Team 1
1 2010.	1 *The Jewel of the Nile*.
2 Woomera.	2 The Nullarbor Plain.
3 Somerset Maugham.	3 Christopher Marlowe.
4 Arnold Bennett.	4 Frederick Marryat.
5 Joel Grey.	5 Diane Keaton.

ROUND 7

Team 2	Team 1
1 The Leaning Tower of Pisa.	1 The Palace of Versailles.
2 None; it's a solo.	2 It was written for baby elephants to perform in a circus ring.
3 1976.	3 1969.
4 Sir Joshua Reynolds.	4 Canaletto.
5 Earth-pig.	5 Wing finger.

ROUND 8

Team 2	Team 1
1 5.	1 7.
2 Sierra Leone. (Lion Mountain Ridge)	2 Anchorage.
3 *Zulu*.	3 Donald Sutherland.
4 The orchid.	4 A small orange.
5 George Washington (Mount Washington).	5 Mount Ararat.

ROUND 9

Team 2	Team 1
1 *Rawhide*.	1 Ty Hardin.
2 The British Museum.	2 Anne of Cleves.
3 Nevil Shute.	3 Sir Walter Scott.
4 3 times a day.	4 Electrocardiogram.
5 26.	5 23.

ROUND 10

Team 2	Team 1
Television	*Religion*
Terry and Bob.	A shamrock.

101

Sport
1981.

Plants
The thrift.

Words
Stir his porridge with it – it's a kitchen utensil.

Team 1

DRINKS ROUND
1 Winchester.

2 Four knights of Henry II.
3 *Mona Lisa*.
4 The Albert Medal.
5 They are bones in the feet.
6 About seven-tenths.
7 Jim Hacker.
8 Anchorage to Nome, Alaska.
9 St Bernadette.
10 India.

RESERVE QUESTIONS
1 St Andrew.
2 Graham Sutherland.
3 German Bight.

Team 2

1 N. Yorkshire (near Skipton).
2 Balthazar Gérard.
3 *A Private Function*.
4 The George Cross.
5 They are bones in the wrist.
6 The Arctic.
7 Michael Aspel.
8 The first surface crossing of the Antarctic.
9 Alicia Markova.
10 Switzerland.

Pub League Quiz 3 Answers

Team 1

Team 2

ROUND 1
1 Grenoble.
2 The microscope.
3 *Iolanthe*.
4 That between Gibraltar and Spain.
5 Horatio Nelson.

1 Chamonix.
2 Celluloid.
3 *The Gondoliers*.
4 Defence Secretary.
5 Paul Revere.

ROUND 2

1	Tannochbrae.	2	New York.
2	Botswana.	2	The west.
3	Cycling (or motor racing).	3	Horse racing.
4	LXXXVIII.	4	MD. (M = 1000 and D = 500).
5	Democracy.	5	Alimony.

ROUND 3

1	*Achille Lauro.*	1	*Rainbow Warrior.*
2	Bob Dylan.	2	Barry Manilow's.
3	Chic Young.	3	Captain Marvel.
4	Ireland's.	4	India.
5	Duncan – King of Scotland.	5	Beatrice.

ROUND 4

1	*Desmond's.*	1	Paul Ford.
2	Buckingham Palace.	2	In front of Buckingham Palace.
3	Switzerland.	3	France (Train Grand Vitesse).
4	Ann Haydon Jones.	4	Liz McColgan.
5	1980.	5	*The Domesday Book.*

ROUND 5

Films
Kiss Me Kate.

Which year?
1959.

Scandal
George IV.

Capitals
Valletta.

Science
A proton.

ROUND 6

1	Carla.	1	Rhea Perlman.
2	The Rosetta Stone.	2	The Piltdown Man.
3	Italy.	3	Vidkun Quisling.
4	Italy.	4	Everton.
5	Bhopal.	5	1987.

ROUND 7

1 Stuffed.

2 Donwell Abbey.
3 Diana Coupland.
4 Sweden.
5 4.

1 The pig – it is a 'raw' smoked ham.
2 *Germinal.*
3 Bob Monkhouse.
4 France.
5 0.

ROUND 8

1 Angling.
2 Violet.
3 Antonio Salieri.
4 361.
5 'Welcome To The Pleasuredome'.

1 Cricket.
2 Deep blue.
3 Thomas Keneally.
4 22.
5 'I am a Woman'.

ROUND 9

1 1981.
2 Thomas Eakins.
3 Gerald Kaufman.
4 Edward Elgar.
5 Huggy Bear.

1 1967.
2 Mary Cassatto.
3 Cecil Parkinson.
4 Monteverdi's.
5 Monty Python.

ROUND 10

Films
Absolute Beginners.

Which year?
1924.

Scandal
Mandy Rice-Davies.

Capitals
Colombo.

Science
An armature.

Team 1

Team 2

DRINKS ROUND

1 Bowls.

2 The Hague, Netherlands.
3 Daphne.
4 Slow.
5 Vistula.

1 It was the first and only dead heat.
2 Organisation of African Unity.
3 Menelaus.
4 Fast.
5 Hudson.

6	A type of anchor.	6	A large rope, or a cable.
7	The Bellamy's.	7	Fenn Street.
8	Edward I.	8	Edward I.
9	Newmarket.	9	Sandown Park.
10	1983.	10	1984.

RESERVE QUESTIONS
1 Sir Ambrose Fleming.
2 The Wellington.
3 Hellebore.

Pub League Quiz 4 Answers

Team 1 | *Team 2*

ROUND 1

1	Delibes.	1	Sibelius.
2	Dr Ramsey.	2	Malcolm X.
3	Seaweeds.	3	A type of bread.
4	Dick Clement and Ian La Frenais.	4	He had six.
5	Eliza Doolittle.	5	Nevil Shute.

ROUND 2

1	A throw in wrestling.	1	Stones, or granites.
2	Southern Africa.	2	Southern India.
3	Mary Astor.	3	Claire Bloom.
4	Ramsay MacDonald.	4	Montezuma.
5	The Goldcrest.	5	The common toad.

ROUND 3

1	Just slip out the back, Jack.	1	John Denver.
2	Dick Whittington.	2	The Marquess of Queensberry's.
3	The Admirable Crichton.	3	Catherine Earnshaw.
4	Edith.	4	The Madonna with the big boobies.
5	Bourbon.	5	Brandy and Cointreau.

ROUND 4

1	The Ku Klux Klan.	1	The Black and Tans.
2	England.	2	Box Lacrosse.
3	*Vertigo*.	3	Joan Crawford.
4	Gunpowder.	4	Mercury.
5	Green.	5	Its gizzard.

ROUND 5

General knowledge
4 pm.

British Prime Ministers
The Liberal Party.

Counties
Avon.

Abbreviations
Peninsular and Oriental.

Space travel
Skylab 2.

Team 2   *Team 1*

ROUND 6

1	Sprinkling with flour or other powder.	1	63 degrees Celsius.
2	Rolf Harris.	2	Johnny Mathis.
3	General.	3	Adelina Patti.
4	*Nabucco*.	4	*Samson and Delilah*.
5	Come Dancing.	5	Major Harry Truscott.

ROUND 7

1	The bowl is level with the jack.	1	Squash.
2	Grill it.	2	Preserved with salt.
3	Captain Hardy.	3	Ellen Terry.
4	Otis Redding.	4	Clarence White.
5	1930.	5	1966.

ROUND 8

1	Colombo.	1	*Bonanza*.
2	Patagonia.	2	Moscow.
3	A Chain Gang.	3	Oddjob.
4	The Atlantic Giant Squid.	4	The humming bird.
5	The rats in 'The Pied Piper of Hamelin'.	5	Winnie-the-Pooh.

ROUND 9

1	Valery Giscard D'Estaing.	**1**	Sir Anthony Blunt.
2	Four.	**2**	Liszt.
3	Westminster Abbey.	**3**	VAT.
4	*Peyton Place*.	**4**	*When the Boat Comes In*.
5	*The Rite of Spring*.	**5**	The Bringer of Old Age.

ROUND 10

General knowledge
Euclid.

British Prime Ministers
Spencer Percival.

Counties
Isle of Wight.

Abbreviations
Fellow of the Royal Academy of Music.

Space travel
Vostock I.

QUIZ 4

Team 1

Team 2

DRINKS ROUND

1	Colombia.	**1**	The Roaring Forties.
2	Mexico.	**2**	Jayne Torvill and Christopher Dean.
3	William Shakespeare's.	**3**	Aberdeen.
4	U2.	**4**	Bryan Adams.
5	*The Shining*.	**5**	*The Enforcer*.
6	Ayesha.	**6**	Horace Rumpole.
7	Pumpkin Pie.	**7**	Sally Lunn.
8	Catalan.	**8**	Baked earth.
9	To make a covered trench, so as to approach a beseiged place.	**9**	A sword.
10	Bates Motel.	**10**	*Love Me Tender*.

RESERVE QUESTIONS

1 The oak.
2 Mountain of Light.
3 *Magic Roundabout*.

Pub League Quiz 5 Answers

Team 1

Team 2

ROUND 1

	Team 1		Team 2
1	Petula Clark.	1	Zager and Evans.
2	'Pippa Passes'.	2	'Leisure'.
3	Poland.	3	New Zealand.
4	Banacek.	4	William Conrad.
5	Methuselah.	5	Sequoia.

ROUND 2

	Team 1		Team 2
1	Mycenae.	1	Doric.
2	The earliest mare in the *General Stud Book*.	2	Water skiing.
3	Egypt's.	3	General Douglas MacArthur.
4	'For All We Know'.	4	'Last Dance'.
5	Sri Lanka.	5	Iceland.

ROUND 3

	Team 1		Team 2
1	8 yards.	1	A player able to bat right-handed or left-handed.
2	At the back of the altar or communion table.	2	Egypt.
3	It was on a raft in the middle of a river.	3	Elba and St Helena.
4	Montreal.	4	West of Alaska, between the Bering Sea and the Pacific Ocean.
5	Jean Louis Géricault.	5	Jacques-Louis David.

ROUND 4

	Team 1		Team 2
1	Connecticut.	1	Kansas.
2	*Peter Grimes*.	2	Pablo Casals.
3	Senior Common Room.	3	Extended Play.
4	A large wild goat.	4	A breed of toy dog.
5	*Going for Gold*.	5	*Krypton Factor*.

ROUND 5

The Bible
Deuteronomy.

Words
Herbs.

Literature
David Storey's.

History
François II, the Dauphin of France.

Sport
Mike Tyson.

Team 2

Team 1

QUIZ
5

ROUND 6

	Team 2		Team 1
1	River Thames.	1	The Mississippi.
2	Stephen Ward.	2	Dr Beeching's.
3	The Who.	3	Led Zeppelin.
4	Ray Milland and Jane Wyman.	4	Ronald Colman and Jane Wyatt.
5	Young Jolyon (Forsyte).	5	Antonio.

ROUND 7

1	Russia.	1	Australia.
2	Carlisle.	2	Canterbury.
3	The Mensheviks.	3	The Iceni.
4	Sheerness.	4	Madison Avenue.
5	1773.	5	1946.

ROUND 8

1	*The Dream of Gerontius.*	1	'Emperor'.
2	Algeria.	2	'Identikit'.
3	It is cold, iced or chilled.	3	Jelly.
4	1924.	4	St Crispin's Day.
5	Rodeo.	5	Roger Black.

ROUND 9

1	German.	1	The Cambodian alphabet (72 letters).
2	Leaving the scene of an accident.	2	Andrew Johnson.
3	The Moluccas.	3	Angkor Thom.
4	Daniel O'Connell.	4	Earl Kitchener of Khartoum.
5	Piano.	5	Violin.

109

ROUND 10

The Bible
Tarsus.

History
Merchant.

Words
Beetles.

Sport
Rod Laver.

Literature
Salman Rushdie.

Team 1	Team 2

DRINKS ROUND

Team 1	Team 2
1 Severing the mooring cables of sea mines.	1 The kukri.
2 Buddy Holly.	2 The Kinks.
3 Olga, Masha and Irina.	3 Becky Sharp.
4 Kent State University, Ohio.	4 Mentmore Towers.
5 Vanuaatu.	5 Hispaniola.
6 Argentina.	6 USA.
7 Bodie.	7 *Highway Patrol*.
8 *The Beggars' Opera*.	8 *Tosca*.
9 R101.	9 Barnes Wallis.
10 Argentina.	10 Thailand.

RESERVE QUESTIONS
1 A game; an indoor form of Quoits.
2 Aeschylus.
3 The Coypu's.

Pub League Quiz 6 Answers

Team 1	Team 2

ROUND 1

Team 1	Team 2
1 12 feet.	1 18 inches.
2 A breed of horse.	2 A bird (a duck).
3 The Emperor Constantine.	3 St Giles.

4   *Kipps* (by H.G. Wells).

5   Cuba.

ROUND 2
1   Cane.
2   David Carradine.
3   U. Thant.
4   Checkers.
5   One.

ROUND 3
1   They are types of chair.

2   The Compass.

3   *Air on a G String*.
4   Pesto.
5   *An Englishman Abroad*.

ROUND 4
1   As US President, he established the 49th parallel as the Canadian–USA border.
2   Pygmy moss.
3   *Gulliver's Travels*.
4   She was donor of the Wightman Cup (as Mrs Wightman).
5   Jacob, his brother.

ROUND 5

Sport
Sundries.

French phrases
Immediately (as soon as possible or with all possible haste).

Opera
Puccini.

4   *The Matchmaker* (Thornton Wilder).
5   Sicily.

1   Vegetable.
2   Robert Mitchum.
3   Trygve Lie.
4   Green.
5   Green.

1   They are some of the world's longest railway tunnels.
2   Ursa Minor (the Little Bear).
3   *The Raindrop Prelude*.
4   Beetroot.
5   Huw Wheldon.

1   A Boeing 707.

2   Corn.
3   *For Whom the Bell Tolls*.
4   The National Stud.

5   Cana.

Literature
Sir Thomas Malory.

Which year?
1974.

Team 2	Team 1

ROUND 6

1	Isadora Duncan.	1	Arnold Bennett.
2	Inigo Jones.	2	John Nash.
3	*Evita.*	3	*Godspell.*
4	−273°C.	4	One calorie.
5	William Blake.	5	Robert Burns.

ROUND 7

1	6th January.	1	1st March.
2	Libya.	2	Czechoslovakia.
3	Alcatraz.	3	Cigarette adverts.
4	*I'm All Right Jack.*	4	*The Lady Vanishes.*
5	Arthur Wing Pinero.	5	J.B. Priestley.

ROUND 8

1	Stirling.	1	Glenfinnan.
2	Delius.	2	Debussy.
3	USA.	3	Belgium.
4	*You Rang M'Lord?.*	4	*Lovejoy.*
5	Britain.	5	Constantine.

ROUND 9

1	Baloo the Bear.	1	Jessica Rabbit.
2	The Wolverene.	2	The Zebra.
3	The Four Tops.	3	'YMCA'.
4	The French Protestants.	4	The Gordon Riots.
5	John Betjeman.	5	Evelyn Waugh.

ROUND 10

Sport
Training.

French phrases
Between ourselves.

Opera
Verdi.

Literature
Madame Defarge.

Which year?
1815.

Team 1	Team 2

DRINKS ROUND

Team 1	Team 2
1 France.	1 Pandit Jawaharlal Nehru.
2 Alice Cooper.	2 Tom Jones.
3 Ronan Point.	3 Aberfan.
4 Kathleen Ferrier.	4 'Greensleeves'.
5 A runaway train (Chapel-en-le-Frith, 1957).	5 The Post Office Railway.
6 The Monmouth Rebellion.	6 Elise Deroche.
7 Tokyo.	7 Staten Island.
8 Gary Player.	8 The PGA.
9 Edith Holden.	9 Joseph Conrad.
10 Lively.	10 At 'walking pace'.

RESERVE QUESTIONS
1 Nelson Rockefeller.
2 8.
3 Ozone.

Pub League Quiz 7 Answers

Team 1	Team 2

ROUND 1

Team 1	Team 2
1 Royal Academy of Dramatic Arts.	1 Port of London Authority.
2 To the fox.	2 Pigs.
3 It was a daytime scene.	3 Cribbage.
4 Methuselah.	4 Andrew.
5 An acid bath.	5 Bluebeard.

ROUND 2

Team 1	Team 2
1 *Cabaret.*	1 *The Man Who Knew Too Much.*
2 24.	2 Rain – it's a rain gauge.
3 Henry VI.	3 Edward II.

4   Catcher.
5   Rheims.

4   Crown green bowls.
5   Paris.

ROUND 3
1   Flanders and Swann.
2   James Michener.
3   Germany.
4   The primrose family.
5   Chopin.

1   Norman Painting.
2   Barry Hines.
3   Spain.
4   The begonia.
5   Vaughan Williams.

ROUND 4
1   An exaltation.
2   Humberside.
3   Andrew Marvell.
4   Humidity.
5   Mick Jagger.

1   A tiding.
2   Cleveland.
3   Alexander Pope.
4   Radiation.
5   Paul McCartney.

ROUND 5

Television
People and Places.

Words
A warning or signal bell.

QUIZ
7

Mythology
He rowed the dead over the
River Styx into Hades.

Sport
Kenny Dalglish.

Literature
Thomas Hardy.

Team 2

Team 1

ROUND 6
1   Tokyo.
2   Maureen O'Hara.
3   Hera.
4   Copenhagen.
5   Light-heavyweight.

1   Las Vegas.
2   George.
3   Juno.
4   Tallinn.
5   Bantamweight and
    featherweight.

ROUND 7
1   Numbers.
2   He led a division of
    Paupers on the First
    Crusade.

1   Romans.
2   David Rizzio.

3 St Catherine.
4 A bird.

5 C.B. Fry.

3 Martinmas.
4 It is a reptile like a crocodile.
5 Ian Botham.

ROUND 8
1 Thunder.
2 The River Towy.
3 Cuba.
4 Rocks.
5 Blackburn Rovers.

1 Going to bed.
2 The Forth.
3 Italy.
4 The science of soils.
5 Ipswich Town.

ROUND 9
1 Sir Michael Horden.
2 The Thrush.
3 A.J. Cronin's.
4 Tapioca.
5 Antonio Stradivari.

1 Will Hay.
2 Hour.
3 Daphne du Maurier's.
4 Sugar cane.
5 Beethoven.

ROUND 10

Television
Scrabble.

Words
A Schoolmaster or Teacher.

Mythology
Weasel.

Sport
Véronique Marot.

Literature
Kingsley Amis.

Team 1

Team 2

DRINKS ROUND
1 Pennsylvania.
2 Norris McWhirter.
3 King Cheops (or Khufu).
4 The breast bone.
5 Glamorgan's.
6 Dead or Alive.
7 The Merry Wives of Windsor.
8 Norway.
9 No sense of smell.
10 Michael Bentine.

1 Oklahoma.
2 Spike Milligan.
3 King Farouk.
4 4.
5 Warwickshire.
6 Adam and the Ants.
7 King Arthur's.
8 Hudson Bay.
9 Walks a tight-rope.
10 Hughie Green.

115

Pub League Quiz 8 Answers

Team 1	**Team 2**

ROUND 1

1	William I.	1	James I.
2	A sea trout.	2	A red worm (used as bait).
3	2000 metres.	3	1745.
4	Uruguay.	4	In Syria.
5	Jane Fonda.	5	Colin Welland.

ROUND 2

1	The violin.	1	The sitar.
2	Dostoyevsky.	2	A.J. Cronin.
3	Goya.	3	Turner.
4	Muscles in the body.	4	The Human Body.
5	Ernesto.	5	Poland.

QUIZ 8

ROUND 3

1	A silver spoon.	1	May be in.
2	Darkness.	2	Nakedness.
3	Bahrain.	3	Zimbabwe.
4	Sheet music.	4	As a writing desk.
5	George Bernard Shaw.	5	Christopher Fry.

ROUND 4

1	20.	1	About 3 miles.
2	Large bombs.	2	A Glider.
3	William III and Mary II.	3	Charles VII.
4	Jim Reeves.	4	Englebert Humperdinck's.
5	DV.	5	1666 (MDCLXVI).

ROUND 5

Quotations
Mark Twain (in *Pudd'nhead Wilson's Calendar*).

Plants
The Daffodil.

Poetry
James Hogg.

Ships and the Sea
Very Large Crude Carrier.

Television
Lech Walesa.

Team 2	Team 1

ROUND 6

1	7.	1	10 feet.
2	Blackberries.	2	Dormouse.
3	Charles II.	3	Henry VIII.
4	Religious music, hymns.	4	Gospel music.
5	T.S. Elliot.	5	W.M. Thackeray.

ROUND 7

1	The *Times Literary Supplement*.	1	Sir William Rees Mogg.
2	Whistling Jack Smith.	2	Tiny Tim.
3	10,000.	3	181 degrees.
4	A bed.	4	Whitstable.
5	Venice's.	5	Geneva.

ROUND 8

1	Dodie Smith.	1	Reverend W. Awdry.
2	Volleyball.	2	Someone who practices Karate.
3	A dog.	3	A large sea bird.
4	Kings Own Scottish Borderers.	4	Territorial Army Volunteer Reserve.
5	Goliath.	5	The Magi.

ROUND 9

1	At the back of the nose and throat.	1	Freckles.
2	2.	2	6 (1 + 2 + 3).
3	The descent of a deity to earth in a bodily form.	3	Momus.

| 4 | *Man of La Mancha.* | 4 | *Carousel.* |
| 5 | *Never Mind the Quality, Feel the Width.* | 5 | 1895. |

ROUND 10

Quotations
Edmond Hoyle (in his 1742 book on Whist).

Plants
Catkins.

Poetry
Tam O'Shanter – in Burns's poem.

Ships and the Sea
The Flying Dutchman.

Television
Optical Reception of Announcements by Coded Line Electronics.

Team 1

Team 2

DRINKS ROUND

1 Stephen Foster.
2 Japan.
3 In 1963.
4 Blood Pressure.
5 Lightfoot.
6 The Government Chief Whip.
7 The Tees.
8 Nicholas Hammond.
9 Polo
10 Childbirth.

1 Henry Lyte.
2 France.
3 In 1967.
4 The Eustachian tubes.
5 Operation Barbarossa.
6 Lord Palmerston.
7 The Isis.
8 Michael Crawford.
9 Orienteering.
10 Food.

RESERVE QUESTIONS

1 In Vienna.
2 Rolls Royce.
3 Forth.

QUIZ
8

Pub League Quiz 9 Answers

Team 1	Team 2

ROUND 1

	Team 1		Team 2
1	Spain.	1	Kenya.
2	Prasutagus.	2	Edward III.
3	Mortimer.	3	Sleeping Beauty.
4	The Battle of Omdurman.	4	The Battle of Marston Moor.
5	W.S. Gilbert.	5	William Langland.

ROUND 2

	Team 1		Team 2
1	The use of words that begin with or include the same letters or sounds.	1	An understatement, often ironical.
2	Introduce Secondary Education for all.	2	Establish freedom of worship.
3	Panama.	3	Haiti.
4	David Lloyd George.	4	Benjamin Disraeli.
5	Hexagonal.	5	Celebrity Squares.

ROUND 3

	Team 1		Team 2
1	Delius.	1	Peter Warlock.
2	Mexico.	2	Belgium.
3	Newts.	3	The Pike.
4	*Billy Liar*.	4	Rooster Cogburn.
5	The Island of Heligoland.	5	Zanzibar.

ROUND 4

	Team 1		Team 2
1	Water.	1	Graphite.
2	John Clare.	2	Robert Frost.
3	Chile and Ecuador.	3	Norway and Russia.
4	Michael Bentine.	4	Bernard Hedges.
5	The ear drum.	5	A finger print.

ROUND 5

Animals	*Television*
It has fin feet.	Bureau des Etrangers.

USA
Alaska.

Science
Sulphuric Acid.

Plays
Christ's suffering and death.

Team 2	Team 1

ROUND 6

1	On a sailing ship. They are sails.	1	A sea bird.
2	Paul Anka.	2	The Bee Gees.
3	It is firm to the teeth.	3	Gorgonzola.
4	*Wasa* (or *Vasa*).	4	Two of the first successful steamships.
5	Lauren Bacall.	5	Audrey Hepburn.

ROUND 7

1	Anita Brookner.	1	William Golding.
2	The Aga Khan ('Shergar').	2	H.R.H. The Duke of Edinburgh.
3	Iran.	3	Albania.
4	*LA Law*.	4	Eddie Shoestring.
5	Periods of Architecture.	5	Breeds of Ducks.

ROUND 8

1	Henry Mayhew.	1	John Osborne's.
2	Fashion.	2	*Hope and Glory*.
3	Dorothy Parker.	3	Oliver Cromwell.
4	Reykjavik.	4	Belize.
5	'Hands across Britain'.	5	Desmond Tutu.

ROUND 9

1	Trente.	1	Quaranta.
2	Burgundy.	2	France.
3	Cambridge University Press.	3	Oxford University Dramatic Society.
4	Haberdasher.	4	Psephologist.
5	1914.	5	1915.

ROUND 10

Animals
Marsupium.

Television
Nicholas Lyndhurst.

USA
Spiro Agnew.

Science
Soda water.

Plays
Volpone.

Team 1	Team 2

DRINKS ROUND

	Team 1		Team 2
1	Lenny Henry.	1	Rob Wilton.
2	Writer's cramp.	2	The inner ear; it's the flap at the entrance to the ear.
3	'Ode to a Nightingale'.	3	Sir Henry Newbolt.
4	Neville Chamberlain.	4	Winston Churchill.
5	Melbourne (1956).	5	Helsinki (1952).
6	Bach's *Air on a G String*.	6	Dvorak's *New World Symphony*.
7	The Los Angeles police.	7	*Marathon Man*.
8	Hercules.	8	Sacred Elephants.
9	The Lark.	9	The mute swan.
10	Torquay United.	10	Stoke City.

RESERVE QUESTIONS
1 Berlin.
2 Will Somers.
3 Originally 'bonefires', where bones were burned.

Pub League Quiz 10 Answers

Team 1	Team 2

ROUND 1

	Team 1		Team 2
1	The Gulf of Bothnia.	1	The Yellow Sea.
2	Pale blue and white.	2	Cream-coloured.
3	Eugene O'Neill.	3	J.M. Synge.
4	Diana Rigg.	4	Patrick Mower.
5	*My Fair Lady*.	5	*Hello Dolly*.

ROUND 2

1	Sir Robert Graham.	1	His wife, Isabella.
2	South Africa.	2	Republic of Ireland.
3	Stitches.	3	A lively dance.
4	The Germans.	4	The Turkish.
5	Brazil.	5	Finland.

ROUND 3

1	Zululand.	1	Haiti.
2	Sweden.	2	USA.
3	Hemlock.	3	Rowena.
4	Patricia Hayes.	4	Nero.
5	Table Tennis.	5	Showjumping.

ROUND 4

1	Suffolk.	1	Cornwall.
2	Edward (975–979).	2	Portugal.
3	The original inhabitants of Jerusalem.	3	Teachers of Law.
4	Geranium.	4	The carnation.
5	Richard Strauss.	5	*Turandot*.

ROUND 5

Sport
Golf.

Pop music
Helen Reddy.

Geography
Portugal.

Art
Van Gogh.

Literature
Oscar Wilde.

Team 2

Team 1

ROUND 6

1	The eye.	1	The bladder.
2	St Matthew.	2	St Luke.
3	Spanish.	3	Anglo-Swiss.
4	Fulham.	4	Shrewsbury.
5	Sparta.	5	Quincy Jones.

ROUND 7

1 Canada.
2 The Hellenes (Greece).
3 Isabella Mary.
4 Behind your ear.
5 8 and 14.

1 Australia.
2 Ceylon (Sri Lanka).
3 Eleanor.
4 The sciatic nerve.
5 1 and 4.

ROUND 8

1 Thomas Hardy.
2 Neptune.
3 Hockenheim.
4 Portsmouth.
5 Walter Matthau.

1 Muriel Spark.
2 Tchaikovsky.
3 Alain Prost.
4 Manchester.
5 Cary Grant.

ROUND 9

1 Steve Davis.
2 Newfoundland.
3 The Congress Party.
4 Officer Dibble.
5 Penguin.

1 Joe Davis.
2 Boston, Massachusetts.
3 Georges Clemenceau.
4 Evil Edna.
5 A snake.

ROUND 10

Sport
Volleyball.

Pop music
Steeleye Span.

Geography
The Gulf of St Lawrence, Quebec.

Art
Paul Gauguin.

Literature
Stan Barstow.

Team 1

Team 2

DRINKS ROUND

1 His nephew.
2 A whirlpool.
3 Sir Oswald Mosley.

4 Al Pacino.
5 A water carrier.

1 Elijah.
2 100.
3 Sir Thomas Stamford Raffles.
4 Albert Finney.
5 It was the first championship fight with gloves.

6 In skiing.	**6** Golf – it's a free shot in a friendly.
7 Dover.	**7** Somerset.
8 Richard Rodgers.	**7** Leonard Bernstein.
9 Anne Boleyn.	**9** Mary, Queen of Scots.
10 *It Ain't Half Hot Mum.*	**10** Sunshine Desserts.

RESERVE QUESTIONS
1 One.
2 Twenty-five.
3 Shirley Bassey.

Pub League Quiz 11 Answers

Team 1   *Team 2*

ROUND 1

1 Belfast.	**1** Chicago.
2 Wind velocity.	**2** A variable electrical resistance.
3 Mountaineering (or Rock Climbing).	**3** Golf.
4 China and North Korea.	**4** Brazil.
5 Rodgers and Hart.	**5** George M. Cohan.

ROUND 2

1 The harp.	**1** The oboe.
2 National League and American League.	**2** Halifax.
3 *Bandwagon.*	**3** David Hamilton.
4 France.	**4** Belgium.
5 University College Hospital (London).	**5** Lord Justice.

ROUND 3

1 Gules.	**1** A broad stripe running the length of the shield.
2 Ray Manzarek.	**2** Kyle MacLachlan.
3 'The Waste Land'.	**3** T.S. Eliot.

QUIZ
11

124

4 Gwynedd.
5 Showing off.

4 Powys.
5 Exaggerating.

ROUND 4
1 Sebastian Coe.
2 Gall Bladder.
3 St Stephen.
4 Hertz.
5 Canadian.

1 Twice.
2 The skull, near the ear.
3 Pius IX (1846–78).
4 The Ohm.
5 British.

ROUND 5

Geography
Athens.

World of Plants
Deadly nightshade.

Animal world
A lizard.

Television
Jon Pertwee.

Poetry
Fair of face.

Team 2

Team 1

ROUND 6
1 Rabat.
3 *A Tale of Two Cities*.
4 Abba.
5 Switzerland.

1 Kinshasa.
3 *The Mill on the Floss*.
4 The Rolling Stones.
5 Italy.

ROUND 7
1 The Grey wolf.
2 Henry VI.
3 Vitamin B_1. (Allow thiamine.)
4 Isaac.
5 A bee-keeper.

1 The Orangutan.
2 Elizabeth I.
3 Vitamin C. (Allow ascorbic acid.)
4 Michael.
5 Mycroft.

ROUND 8
1 Peter Finch.
2 Crécy.
3 Crow.
4 Lillian Hellman.
5 Cherilyn Sakisian.

1 Barbara Stanwyck.
2 Shrewsbury.
3 A shell-fish.
4 T.S. Eliot.
5 Salvatore Bono.

QUIZ
11

125

ROUND 9

1 Peru.
2 He collected taxes.
3 Pelé.
4 Oedipus.
5 The Semi-quaver.

1 Turkey.
2 Jeremiah's.
3 Emil Zatopek.
4 King Idris.
5 A Semi-breve.

ROUND 10

Geography
San Juan.

World of Plants
The Bilberry.

Animal world
The salmon.

Television
Gibbs SR Toothpaste.

Poetry
Rudyard Kipling.

Team 1

Team 2

DRINKS ROUND

1 Schubert.
2 William III (William of Orange).
3 India.
4 5.30 pm.
5 Rugby Union.
6 Simon Ward.
7 A breed of duck.
8 Vera Brittain.
9 Indiana.
10 Los Angeles, California.

1 Chopin.
2 Richard I.

3 New Hampshire.
4 9.00 pm.
5 Wood-breaking.
6 Angie Dickinson.
7 A fish – like a pike.
8 Hugh Gaitskell.
9 Virginia.
10 Houston, Texas.

RESERVE QUESTIONS

1 1966.
2 Wagner.
3 Samson.

QUIZ
11

126

Pub League Quiz 12 Answers

Team 1

Team 2

ROUND 1

1 John de Balliol – Chosen King of Scotland 1292.
2 Greece.
3 Compulsory figures.
4 *Brideshead Revisited*.
5 Charles Luciano.

1 George, Prince Regent (later, George IV).
2 Corfu.
3 Ice Dancing.
4 *Pickwick Papers*.
5 George Kelly.

ROUND 2

1 Rubens.
2 Dublin.
3 Vivaldi.
4 8 yards.
5 29th May.

1 Sir Joshua Reynolds.
2 Cardiff.
3 Enrique Granados.
4 30 yards.
5 28th December.

ROUND 3

1 The Move.
2 Ogden Nash.
3 Thomas.
4 The rock and soil debris deposited by a glacier.
5 Nevada.

1 Sweet.
2 George Bernard Shaw.
3 Changing water into wine.
4 Yellowish-grey loam soil.
5 Louisiana.

ROUND 4

1 Newmarket.
2 Alexandre Dumas (the elder).
3 The oboe.
4 Charles II.
5 Whoopi Goldberg.

1 Aintree.
2 Pushkin.
3 Sir John Barbirolli.
4 Henry VIII.
5 The Sunshine Cab Company.

QUIZ
12

ROUND 5

Places
Porcelain (or China).

Politics
Israel's.

Science
Very low temperatures.

Words
The female 'Fates' of
Scandinavian mythology.

Books
It is a reference book of
British nobility.

Team 2 | *Team 1*

ROUND 6
1 Dutch.
2 Cello.
3 Lord Wolseley.
4 They are brother and
   sister.
5 The Golden poppy.

1 Ancient British.
2 Organ.
3 Admiral Duncan.
4 Table tennis.
5 Orange blossom.

ROUND 7
1 Spanish Civil War.
2 Scotland.
3 Gilbert and Sullivan.
4 *The Winter's Tale*.
5 Pigeon racing.

1 Indian Mutiny.
2 North-west Spain.
3 Johann Strauss (the
   younger).
4 *As You Like It*.
5 Polo.

ROUND 8
1 Geneviève.
2 King John.
3 Lutetia.
4 The Joule.
5 'Pearls Before Swine'.

1 Isidore the Labourer.
2 Henry I.
3 Gades.
4 The Coulomb.
5 'The Average White
   Band'.

ROUND 9
1 Out of condition to fight.
2 In Corfe Castle, Dorset.
3 Barbara Cartland.
4 Ancient British and Irish
   alphabet.
5 *Evita*.

1 A deputy.
2 Lincoln.
3 Iran.
4 An object made of wood.
5 Frankie Laine.

ROUND 10

Places
New York State Prison.

Politics
Spain.

Science
Heavy water.

Words
He is a dealer in horses.

Books
Hilaire Belloc.

Team 1	Team 2

DRINKS ROUND

	Team 1			Team 2
1	M20.		1	M11.
2	Republic of Ireland.		2	The USA.
3	Mary Tudor, Queen Mary I.		3	Queen Victoria.
4	Pope John Paul II.		4	Prince Charles.
5	Posy Simmonds.		5	*The Guardian.*
6	A hare.		6	A snake.
7	The New Seekers.		7	Herman and the Hermits.
8	Spain.		8	Italy.
9	Amsterdam.		9	Lisbon.
10	Sir Geoffrey de Havilland.		10	R.J. Mitchell.

RESERVE QUESTIONS
1 *Pilgrim's Progress.*
2 31st December.
3 630.

Pub League Quiz 13 Answers

Team 1	Team 2

ROUND 1

	Team 1			Team 2
1	American Standard Code for Information Interchange.		1	International Civil Aviation Organization.

2	Howard Spring.	2	Judith Krantz.
3	Enoch.	3	He was a shepherd.
4	Tchaikovsky's.	4	Chopin.
5	The Peacock (on to his tail).	5	The Straits of Gibraltar.

ROUND 2

1	The Isle of Man.	1	Guiseley, W. Yorks. (Harry Ramsden's.)
2	Helsinki.	2	Grenoble, France.
3	Marvin Gaye.	3	Roger Miller.
4	*Citizen Kane.*	4	*The Absent Minded Professor.*
5	The River Soar.	5	The Dee.

ROUND 3

1	Paraguay.	1	Georgetown.
2	Liechtenstein.	2	Sarawak.
3	Nijinsky.	3	Churchill Downs (Louisville, Kentucky).
4	Thomas Hardy.	4	Emile Zola.
5	The Orchid.	5	Nicotiana.

ROUND 4

1	Melvyn Hayes.	1	Archie Bunker.
2	In Syria.	2	The Ionian Islands.
3	A member of the clergy.	3	Cloaks or Capes.
4	A large flightless bird.	4	A chocolate drop (or other sweetmeat).
5	Appomattox.	5	The Second.

ROUND 5

Sport
The Derby, The St Leger and the 2000 Guineas.

Composers
Richard Strauss.

History
The production and sale of alcoholic drinks.

Art
The Boyhood of Raleigh.

Poems
'Lepanto' (Chesterton).

Team 2	Team 1

ROUND 6

	Team 2		Team 1
1	Dorothy L. Sayers.	1	L. Frank Baum.
2	Edward the Confessor (in 1066).	2	Richard III.
3	Borneo.	3	Greece.
4	In the wrist.	4	In the thigh.
5	Badminton.	5	New Zealand.

ROUND 7

1	1000.	1	100.
2	Russia.	2	The *Admiral Graf Spee*.
3	Abraham.	3	Jethro.
4	Jackson Pollock.	4	Sir Gilbert Scott.
5	Queen's Park.	5	10,000 metres.

ROUND 8

1	The throne of Spain.	1	The throne of Denmark.
2	His friend Julian.	2	*The Archers*.
3	A Blacksmith.	3	Linen weaver.
4	Brazil.	4	Zambia.
5	The Battle of Agincourt.	5	The Battle of Lewes.

ROUND 9

1	Samuel Johnson.	1	Ned Kelly's.
2	Denmark.	2	Norway.
3	Motorcycling.	3	$1/8$ inch.
4	*Son of Kong*.	4	*Bonzo Goes to College*.
5	*The Barber of Seville*.	5	Franco Alfano.

ROUND 10

Sport
Alec and Eric Bedser.

Art
Titian.

Composers
Paderewski.

Poems
Alfred, Lord Tennyson.

History
Louis XIV.

Team 1	Team 2

DRINKS ROUND

Team 1	Team 2
1 The Ellice Islands.	1 Northern Rhodesia.
2 Claude Rains.	2 Charlie Chaplin.
3 17.	3 21.
4 Thomas Jefferson.	4 Velasquez.
5 C.S. Lewis.	5 Sinclair Lewis.
6 Charles II.	6 His son Edward VI, aged 10.
7 Vilnius.	7 In the Persian Gulf.
8 A male falcon.	8 The grebe family.
9 Table Tennis.	9 West Ham United.
10 Oedipus.	10 Orpheus.

RESERVE QUESTIONS
1 Lammas.
2 Oscar Wilde.
3 Ken Dodd.

Pub League Quiz 14 Answers

Team 1	Team 2

ROUND 1

Team 1	Team 2
1 Bach.	1 Percy Grainger.
2 Tanks.	2 Hermann Goering.
3 Spain.	3 Burgundy.
4 'Composed upon Westminster Bridge' (Wordsworth).	4 'Hyperion' (Keats).
5 Bayview.	5 James Darren and Robert Colbert.

ROUND 2

Team 1	Team 2
1 Harry Dacre.	1 Henry Mancini.
2 12 ft × 6ft 1½ in.	2 9 ft × 5 ft.
3 1801.	3 1968.

4 Steeleye Span.	**4** Creedence Clearwater Revival.
5 Triple Black.	**5** Hard Black.

ROUND 3

1 The Boers and the Zulus.	**1** Carthage and Rome.
2 Athene.	**2** Noah.
3 1976.	**3** 1964.
4 Moses.	**4** Moses.
5 Lesotho.	**5** Niger.

ROUND 4

1 A monster with a lion's head a goat's body and a serpent tail.	**1** Thor – it was his hammer.
2 Rimsky-Korsakov.	**2** Gian-Carlo Menotti.
3 Goya.	**3** The Duchess of Alva.
4 Pedro Alvares Cabral.	**4** Hernando de Soto.
5 The 'snatch' and the 'clean and jerk'.	**5** Cross-country skiing and shooting.

ROUND 5

Television
Peckham.

Pop music
Pink Floyd.

Famous People
He wrote 'The Star Spangled Banner' (in 1814).

History
William Rufus.

Animals
A wild llama.

Team 2

Team 1

ROUND 6

1 Ribonucleic acid.	**1** Deoxyribonucleic acid.
2 Mehmed VI.	**2** Henry IV.
3 At the most southerly point of India.	**3** Antarctica.
4 Paul Scott.	**4** Jonathan Swift.
5 *Christ on the Mount of Olives*.	**5** Handel.

ROUND 7

1 *The Four Horsemen of the Apocalypse*.
2 Mumtaz Mahal (wife of Shah Jahan).
3 Robert Koch.
4 Jim Sullivan (in 1925).

5 Eastern Capital.

1 *The Gay Divorce* (1934).

2 Sir Benjamin Hall.

3 Antoine Henri Becquerel.
4 Wilfred Rhodes (for England, aged 52 years).
5 Edo.

ROUND 8

1 Tracey and Sharon.
2 Between Greenland and Iceland.
3 Tobias Smollett.
4 Brinley Richards.
5 The arm.

1 Ivan Fox.
2 Between Nova Scotia and New Brunswick, Canada.
3 Edgar Allan Poe.
4 Joseph Haydn.
5 The brain.

ROUND 9

1 Programmable Read Only Memory.

2 The potato.
3 Peter Nichols.
4 Parmigianino (also known as Parmigiano).
5 Norman Dagley.

1 Beginners All-purpose Symbolic Instruction Code.
2 Antiseptic surgery.
3 Erich Maria Remarque.
4 Roy Lichtenstein.

5 The San Francisco 49ers.

ROUND 10

Television
Garfield Morgan.

History
Theodoric the Great.

Famous People
Ras Tafari.

Animals
A fish.

Pop music
Chaka Khan.

Team 1

Team 2

DRINKS ROUND

1 Bolivia and Paraguay.

1 New Zealand colonists and the Maoris.

2 The S.I. unit of electromagnetic inductance.
3 Doha.
4 Julie Walters.
5 A murder.
6 The giant Loki.
7 Paganini.
8 In Switzerland.
9 Gordon Burns.
10 John Dryden.

2 The S.I. unit of illuminance.
3 Windhoek.
4 Sir Henry Irving.
5 A sleuth.
6 Bellerophon.
7 Chopin.
8 In Brazil.
9 Tony Robinson.
10 Sir John Betjeman.

RESERVE QUESTIONS
1 New York.
2 Alaska.
3 Short Take Off and Landing Airport.